DUESENBERG MOTORS, INC.

DUESENBERG II® TORPEDO PHAETON

Torpedo Phaeton

Murphy Roadster

Duesenberg Motors, Inc. offers five models of the modern classic Duesenberg II® automobile for the discriminating collector and car enthusiast. Exact in design, scale, and quality craftsmanship to the original, each automobile is custom crafted to order as a unique statement of elegance, luxury, and hand-built quality that matches the timeless style of the 1930's most expensive car. While matching the original appearance features, each Duesenberg II® has the convenience and safety of a modern drive train and comfort features, making it a pleasure to drive - whether across town or across the country.

D1127785

00

The Royalton

Speedster

Torpedo Roadster

Torpedo Sedan

The Duesenberg®
Estate Golf Car

Duesenberg II®
Specifications

Duesenberg II®
Details

Legal Information

From its introduction in December 1928 till the last car was built in 1937, the original Duesenberg® was the finest car in the world, both in quality, design and in performance. Also the most expensive car in the world, Duesenberg® was the standard for luxury automobiles and sold only to the very affluent, including movie stars. Since the last Duesenberg® was delivered 60 years ago, the value of the original cars has risen to the million dollar range and the mystique of this rare and beautiful work of automotive art has continued to make the name Duesenberg® the most recognized for the ultimate in quality and value.

We custom build five models of the Duesenberg II® - the boattail Speedster, Torpedo Roadster, Royalton, Murphy Roadster, and Torpedo Phaeton; investment in these hand-built classics starts at $195,000.00 (U.S.). We are in the process of introducing the ultimate new model for the serious collector - the Duesenberg II® Torpedo Sedan. The original Torpedo Sedan was built for the 1933 Chicago World's Fair, and was the most luxurious and expensive Duesenberg® ever built.

We also offer the Duesenberg® Estate Golf Car, which has many of the features of the automobiles and is ideally suited to use on the golf course, estate, or special event. The Estate is available in two or four passenger models, with a wide variety of optional features. Built to be a prized possession for the discerning estate owner, avid golfer, and classic car enthusiast alike, each car is custom crafted to your personal specifications.

DUESENBERG MOTORS, INC.

P.O. BOX 66 • One Heritage Lane • Elroy, WI 53929 • U.S.A. • Telephone (608) 462-8100 • Fax (608) 462-8997

Contact E-mail : info@duesenbergmotors.com

MURPHY ROADSTER | TORPEDO PHAETON | ESTATE GOLF CAR
SPECIFICATIONS | DETAILS | LEGAL INFORMATION

Promoted and Hosted by: ACE
Last updated on 01/07/2000

Museum of the City of San Francisco

Home   Index   By Subject   By Year   Biographies   The Gift Shop

Ultimate San Francisco "Jazz Age" symbol was the Duesenberg automobile, as advertised in a 1925 edition of the *San Francisco News Letter*. Columns in the background suggest the photograph was taken at the Palace of Fine Arts.

BUILT TO OUTCLASS, OUTRUN AND OUTLAST ANY CAR ON THE ROAD

A Rare Jewel!

MASTER craftsmen work for six months to build a Duesenberg.

Slowly, with a watchmaker's precision, each part is assembled and each body line fashioned.

Naturally, production is very limited. But the Duesenberg owner can ever appreciate the fact that he possesses a motor car creation ranking in the same class as an original painting or rare jewel.

"The Grand Prix Car"

LLOYD S. JOHNSON COMPANY
1930 VAN NESS AVENUE
SAN FRANCISCO

DUESENBERG
THE ORIGINAL STRAIGHT EIGHT

Return to top of page

the world of automobiles

An Illustrated Encyclopedia of the Motor Car

COLUMBIA HOUSE/New York

Consultant Editor: Tom Northey
Executive Editor: Ian Ward
Editorial Director: Brian Innes
Assistant Editors: Laurie Caddell
Mike Winfield
Art Editor: David Goodman
Picture Research: Evan Davies
Cover Design: Harry W. Fass
Production Manager: Warren Bright

contributors
ANDY ANDERSON: Drag Racing
DAVID BURGESS WISE:
Daimler, Gottlieb
Daimler GB
Darracq
Davis
Decauville
De Dietrich
De Dion-Bouton
Delaunay-Belleville
Dennis
Derby
De Soto
DFP
Diatto
Dodge
Duesenberg
Dunkley
Dunlop
Duryea
Edge
Edsel
Electric Cars
Enfield
JEFF DANIELS: Datsun
JOHN HELLER: Dangerous Driving
PETER HULL: Delage
Delahaye

MIKE KETTLEWELL:
Daytona
De Palma
Dutch Grand Prix
TOM NORTHEY: Davrian
L. J. K. SETRIGHT: Dampers
De Dion Suspension
Diesel
Differential
Dynamometer
MIKE TWITE: De Tomaso
DKW
Donohue
East African Safari
Elva
IAN WARD: Decarbonising
Dynamo

Picture acknowledgments
Page 481: National Motor Museum; Von Fersen; Italfoto—482: Von Fersen; Von Fersen; National Motor Museum—483: Von Fersen—484: Boschetti; National Motor Museum—485: National Motor Museum—486: National Motor Museum; National Motor Museum; Boschetti; Boschetti—487: National Motor Museum; National Motor Museum; Boschetti; Boschetti—488: Boschetti; Quattroruote; Daimler—489: Daimler—490: L. J. Caddell—492: L. J. Caddell— 493: Italfoto; National Motor Museum—494: Alfa Romeo; Belli—495: Bisconcini—496: Keystone; London Art Tech; N. Bruce—497: N. Bruce—498: Datsun—499: S. Davis—500: Davrian—501: London Art Tech—502: London Art Tech—503: London Art Tech—504: Popular Motoring—505: Popular Motoring—506: Italfoto—507: Von Fersen; Von Fersen; National Motor Museum—508: Turin Museum—509: Conway/Cherrett; Conway/Cherrett; Von Fersen; National Motor Museum—510: Coluzzi; Boschetti; Boschetti—511: C. Barker; Boschetti; Boschetti—512: Italfoto; ICP; Italfoto—513: Italfoto; Boschetti; Boschetti—514: Quattroruote; Quattroruote; Quattroruote; Belli—515: Boschetti—517:
Boschetti; Italfoto—518: Cherrett—519: N. Bruce; N. Bruce; Belli; ICP—520: Cherrett; Belli—521: Bisconcini; National Motor Museum—522: National Motor Museum; Belli; Boschetti—523: Boschetti; G. Goddard—524: Quattroruote; National Motor Museum—525: National Motor Museum—526: Belli—527: National Motor Museum—528: Agostini; National Motor Museum—529: Boschetti—530: Boschetti—531: Papetti; Quattroruote; Quattroruote—532: Quattroruote; Zagari—533: Quattroruote—534: National Motor Museum—535: National Motor Museum—536: Boschetti—537: Quattroruote; Mercedes-Benz—540: Scania—542: Papetti—543: Boschetti; Papetti; Quattroruote; Quattroruote; Quattroruote—544: Audi—545: Quattroruote; Quattroruote; Quattroruote; Quattroruote; Von Fersen—546: Quattroruote; Quattroruote—548: Quattroruote—549: Audi—550: Belli; Belli; Quattroruote; Belli—551: National Motor Museum—552: Popperfoto; Quattroruote; Quattroruote; Quattroruote—553: Quattroruote; Popperfoto—554: Chrysler—555: Ludvigsen—556: Chrysler—557: Chrysler—558: Chrysler—559: London Art Tech—560: London Art Tech—561: Marka—562: Quattroruote—563: Marka; Race Reporters—565: Quattroruote; Picturepoint; Race Reporters; Race Reporters; Race Reporters; Race Reporters—566: Quattroruote; Quattroruote; Belli—567: Belli—568: Belli; Quattroruote—569: Belli—570: Belli—571: National Motor Museum—572: Quattroruote; Belli—573: Burgess Wise—574: Dunlop—575: Dunlop—576: Belli; National Motor Museum—577: National Motor Museum—578: G. Goddard—579: G. Goddard—580: London Art Tech; G. Goddard—582: L. J. Caddell—583: Fiat—584: London Art Tech; Keystone—585: Keystone—586/587: Keystone—587: London Art Tech—588: London Art Tech—589: National Motor Museum; Burgess Wise—590: National Motor Museum; Quattroruote; Quattroruote—591: National Motor Museum—592: Quattroruote; National Motor Museum—593: National Motor Museum—594: National Motor Museum; Belli—595: Quattroruote; Quattroruote; Fiat; Popperfoto—596: Fiat; Quattroruote; Fiat—597: Phipps; Trojan—598: Quattroruote; Trojan—599: Veteran Vintage Motor Museum; National Motor Museum—600: National Motor Museum—cover: Belli; National Motor Museum.

Contents   Page

FOUNDER OF THE FOUR-WHEELER

IT WAS DEAD OF NIGHT on an autumn evening in 1883, yet the shed at the bottom of the garden of number 13 Gartenstrasse, in the German spa town of Bad Cannstatt, was a hive of activity. From inside came the clink and rattle of machinery. Suddenly, another noise disturbed the night air, the clatter of boots on the garden path as a detachment of the Royal Württemberg Police Force marched up to the door. The inspector rapped sharply on the wood, and the door was opened by a portly middle-aged man with a neat beard.

'Gottlieb Daimler,' said the inspector, 'your neighbours have laid a complaint that they strongly suspect you of being involved in the manufacture of counterfeit banknotes. I have a warrant to search your workshop.'

A few minutes later, however, the police withdrew, apologising profusely, having discovered that, far from being a coiner, Daimler was just an inventor, who seemed to be working on some kind of engine. Though how he expected it to run without a boiler, goodness only knew.

What the inspector and his minions failed to realise, though, was that they had been looking at a power unit that represented the culmination of a 25-year search for a self-contained motive force that would supplant the steam engine.

Gottlieb Daimler was born on 17 March 1834, at Schorndorf, in the Rems Valley, 'Württemberg's little Garden of Paradise'. His father ran a bakery and wine bar but, from an early age, his son showed great interest in technology. He graduated from the local Latin school in 1848, and went into apprenticeship with a carbine manufacturer named Raithel, whose products were in great demand, owing to the wave of revolution that was then sweeping through Germany. Four years later, Gottlieb passed his craft test by making a pair of double-barrelled pistols with rifled barrels and engraved handles; and left gunsmithing behind him for ever.

He enrolled at the School for Advanced Training in the Industrial Arts at Stuttgart, under Ferdinand Steinbeis. The course was essentially practical, the students working at a factory all day and studying industrial mechanics at the school every evening, as well as on Sunday mornings. In 1853, Steinbeis found Daimler a job with the firm of F. Rollé and Schwilque at Grafenstaden, near Strasbourg; the works was known as 'the Factory College', because the manager, Friedrich Messmer, was a former teacher at the Karlsruhe Institute of Technology and was now devoting his skills to the advanced training of promising young engineers. The work was hard, the day often stretching from 5 am well into the night, but Daimler thrived on it. When the company began building railway locomotives in 1856, the 22-year-old Daimler was promoted to foreman.

He felt, however, that he lacked sufficient knowledge of engineering, and took a two years' leave of absence to study engineering design at the Stuttgart Polytechnical Institute. He came through this with a thorough knowledge of locomotive technology and a profound conviction that the future lay with a source, other than steam. What he envisaged was a small, cheap, easy-to-run engine which could be afforded by light industry; a development perhaps of the crude gas engines which were just making their debut.

In the summer of 1861, Daimler resigned from the Grafenstaden firm to follow his dream. After a brief visit to Paris, he moved to England, where he spent a year working with leading engineering companies, gaining much experience in the use of machine tools. The climax of his visit came in 1862 with a visit to the London World Fair, where among the scientific and technical exhibits were a couple of steam carriages.

When he returned to Germany, Daimler's

Below left: after much experimenting, Gottlieb Daimler's first four-wheeled vehicle was ready by 1886 and made its initial trial runs around the Cannstatt area

Below: in 1892, Gottlieb Daimler produced this air-cooled, V-twin engine with spray carburettor and hot-tube ignition

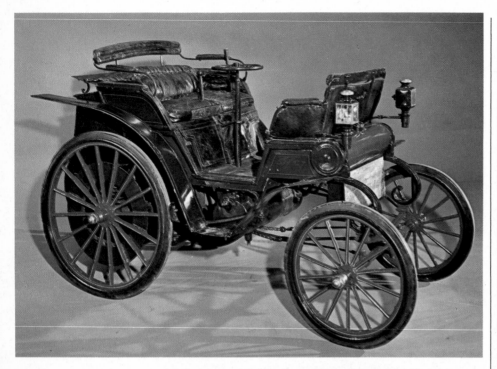

Above: by 1895, Daimler and Maybach had settled their differences with the Daimler Motoren-Gesellschaft and were producing this twin-cylinder, belt-driven *vis-à-vis* tourer

Right: in 1897, the *vis-à-vis* was replaced by the Phönix, the first Daimler to be produced with the engine situated in front

ambitions were running on modest lines: he wanted to set up a factory to build machine tools and small woodworking machinery such as he had seen in England.

For a while, he worked at the Maschinenfabrik Straub in Geislingen, designing mills, tools and turbines. Then, at the recommendation of his old tutor, Steinbeis, Daimler took over the management of Bruderhaus Reutlingen, an offshoot of a charitable institution founded in 1837 to combine modern industrialism with a socialism based on Christian brotherly love. The Reutlingen factory made machinery for paper mills, farm machinery and weighbridges but, the theories of socialism proved incapable of being applied to the profitable running of a business and, by 1863, the Bruderhaus was in trouble. The creditors' organisation hired Daimler first as an inspector, then as a member of the executive committee but, although Daimler's administration showed modest profits, he found the work frustrating, and resigned at the end of June 1869.

At the time, the period Daimler spent at the Bruderhaus seemed to have been wasted, but it had brought him into contact with a gifted young

engineer named Wilhelm Maybach, who had entered the Bruderhaus as a fifteen-year-old orphan in 1861.

When, in July 1869, Daimler was appointed director of the factories of the Maschinenbau Gesellschaft Karlsruhe, he sent for Maybach to come and work for him. Although Daimler was a first-class organiser, it seems that Maybach had a far more original mind, and was capable of coming up with the practical solutions to Daimler's abstract conceptions. Having set the Karlsruhe works on an even keel, Daimler was offered a job which at last seemed to give him the chance to realise his ambition of developing a new power source.

The Otto and Langen Company had been reorganised as the Gasmotoren-Fabrik Deutz in 1872 to produce an improved version of Otto's atmospheric gas engine; the company needed an experienced factory manager to get production under way, and chose Daimler in preference to Otto himself. In August 1872, Daimler took over his new job; on his recommendation, Maybach was appointed chief designer.

Within three years, production had grown to

634 engines annually, but the Otto engine had reached the peak of its development—its vertically acting free piston needed a headroom of ten to thirteen feet, yet the engine developed no more than three horsepower—and the company found that they had expanded their factory to a far greater extent than the incoming orders warranted.

Something had to be done to stave off the impending crisis, and Daimler, who was still obstinately in favour of the atmospheric engine, was not the man to do it. However, one of his protégés, Franz Rings, helped Otto set up a research department to continue the search for a four-stroke engine that Otto had abandoned in 1862. Hermann Schumm, another Daimler man, developed working prototypes of Otto and Rings' new engine within a few months of the first drawings being completed; the first engines were tested in the autumn of 1876. Despite its crude ignition arrangements, with a slide valve exposing a flame to the compressed gas/air mixture at the crucial moment, the Otto four-stroke engine proved an immediate success.

Otto and Daimler were, however, both strong-willed men, and the friction between these two obstinate personalities led to disagreements. Things came to a head in 1881, when Daimler was sent on a trip to Russia to study the market for gas engines there. On his return, he was offered the chance of setting up a Deutz branch office in St Petersburg—or resigning. He left, followed shortly after by the faithful Maybach, and set up on his own in Cannstatt, living on his savings and on the income from the shares he still

held in the Deutz company.

One of Daimler's objectives was to simplify the design of the engine by doing away with the clumsy, complicated slide-valve ignition but, mistrusting electricity, he chose to develop the inflexible hot-tube ignition, invented by Leo Funck, of Aachen. Daimler's engine had a thin-walled tube projecting into the cylinder. The outer end, which was closed, was kept almost at white heat by a bunsen burner; part of the explosive mixture produced by the carburettor was forced into the tube by the rising piston and combustion took place.

As there was absolutely no control over the ignition timing, Daimler and Maybach had many setbacks before they could persuade the engine to run properly. The results, recalled Daimler, were initially quite hopeless. Premature firing of the mixture occurred again and again when the engine was being started and during compression, before reaching dead centre, when the flywheel was suddenly, and unexpectedly, thrown backwards instead of forwards, the crank ripping right out of the experiment assistant's hand like a bolt of lightning.

Eventually, however, Daimler and Maybach sorted out the ignition problems, finding that the little engine could run at speeds of 450 to 900 rpm which was the maximum of other forms of gas engine. Daimler saw this engine as a universal power unit, for industry as well as for vehicles; nevertheless, he was experimenting with a mobile test bench in November 1885. For the sake of cheapness, he fitted the vertical, half-horsepower engine in a wooden boneshaker

bicycle frame steadied by outrigger wheels. Once he had determined that his engine would drive a vehicle, he abandoned the boneshaker and began work on a horseless carriage. Having developed a 1.1 hp engine for this new project, he ordered a four-seater phaeton from the coach-builders Wimpff and Son of Stuttgart.

As he wanted his plans to remain secret as long as possible, Daimler told Wimpff that the carriage was a birthday present for his wife, and that he wanted it 'handsome, but very solidly built'. When the vehicle arrived, Daimler sent it to the Esslingen Engineering Works to have the engine installed. The power unit was coupled to the rear wheels through a simple two-ratio belt-drive, which rotated a countershaft with pinions at each end engaging in toothed rings attached to the rear wheels. Although the carriage seems to have performed satisfactorily, there was still much popular prejudice against self-propelled road vehicles, and Daimler's initial successes came from orders for engines for motor boats and rail carriages—he even supplied power units for some pioneer airships, as well as stationary engines which were fitted in mobile saw benches and fire pumps.

Demand for Daimler engines grew rapidly, and more production space was found by moving out of the garden workshop into a former nickel-plating works nearby.

Now Daimler and Maybach began work on a new power unit, a V-twin which gave a greatly increased power-to-weight ratio within similar dimensions (although the V-twin layout itself was not new, having been used on light steam engines).

Maybach designed a car—the 'steel-wheeler' —round this engine, and both power unit and car were shown at the 1889 Paris World Exhibition, resulting in the signing of a sales agreement with Panhard and Levassor, who sold engines to Peugeot.

Above left: the Cannstatt Daimler built in 1899. A year later, on 6 March 1900, Gottlieb Daimler died

Above: the PD-wagen of 1900 was designed by Gottlieb Daimler's son, Paul, and featured a twin-cylinder, 1410 cc engine, developing 8 bhp at 850 rpm

To acquire the capital necessary for further expansion, Daimler signed contracts with a gun-powder manufacturer named Max Duttenhofer and another industrialist, W. Lorenz, which resulted in the formation of the Daimler-Motoren-Gesellschaft on 28 November 1890. The parnership quickly turned sour, however, and, at the end of 1892, Daimler and Maybach cut loose and set up an experimental workshop in the great summer hall of the defunct Hotel Hermann in Cannstatt. They developed a high-speed, two-cylinders-in-line engine, the Phönix, fitted with Maybach's new invention, the spray carburettor (which was really rather wasted on the inflexible tube-ignition power unit) and a belt-driven car of hippomobile inelegance, which was wildly out of date compared with the Daimler-engined cars being built by Panhard and Peugeot.

At the end of 1895, truce was declared between Daimler, Maybach and the Daimler Motoren-Gesellschaft, and serious production of Phönix-engined cars began. After a couple of years, however, Gottlieb Daimler's health began to break down. As his powers deteriorated, so Maybach emerged from the background and, helped by Daimler's son, Paul, began development of a new type of car for the wealthy Austrian, Emil Jellinek.

They called this new car the Mercedes, the 'car of the day after tomorrow', but it was a day that dawned too late for Gottlieb Daimler, who died on 6 March 1900, before the agreement to produce the new model had been finalised. DBW

LIMOUSINES FIT FOR KINGS AND NOBILITY

Daimler cars have slowly lost their identity. Once upon a time, though, Daimlers were the choice of both royalty and nobility

UNDERNEATH THE ARCHES—that was where the story of Daimler in Britain really started. It was all due to the foresight of Frederick Richard Simms, a young mechanical engineer from Warwickshire. Simms had met Gottlieb Daimler at the Bremen Exhibition at the end of the 1880s, a meeting which resulted in Simms acquiring all Daimler engine patent rights for the United Kingdom and colonies (except Canada). In 1891, Simms borrowed a petrol-engined launch from Daimler and gave demonstrations on the Thames at Putney.

There was, thought Simms, scope for a more ambitious marketing venture, so in May 1893 he was responsible for the formation of the Daimler Motor Syndicate Limited, which fitted engines into launches in a railway arch under Putney Bridge railway station. After the Daimler-engined Panhard and Peugeot cars had swept the board at the 1894 Paris-Rouen Trials, Simms decided that the time had come to establish a motor-car factory in Britain.

In the summer of 1895, the first Daimler-engined car arrived in England, and the British Motor Syndicate was formed, having purchased the rights from Simms, to exploit the Daimler patents within the British Empire, and start manufacturing in Britain. One of the syndicate's members was the infamous Harry J. Lawson, who had learned the art of company

flotation from Terah Hooley, whose name had become a byword for the promotion of firms with vastly over-inflated share capitals.

Lawson, the son of a Brighton clergyman, saw rich pickings in the new locomotion, and in January 1896 he floated the Daimler Motor Company: his eventual aim was to control the entire British motor industry, to which end he set about securing every motor patent available, squandering vast sums on worthless projects like the Pennington engine. Lawson's directors, after a Continental junket in which French and German car factories were studied, set about finding a suitable British factory. After fruitless inspections of conditions at Cheltenham and Birmingham, they heard of a disused cotton mill at Coventry, which was acquired in April 1896. Production did not get under way until early in 1897, before which time the company's activities consisted of screwing Lawson's patent plate on to imported Panhards and Cannstatt-Daimlers. Neither was the Daimler Motor Company the sole occupant of the Motor Mills, which it shared with the Great Horseless Carriage Company (later the Motor Manufacturing Company) and some Pennington activity.

Indeed, it was almost impossible to distinguish between Daimler and MMC products: the two companies were interdependent, Daimler making the

TO THE NOBILITY & GENTRY
MAY 1896

THE GREAT HORSELESS CARRIAGE Co Ltd

HAS THE HONOUR TO PRESENT

...EL which is propelled by an
...L COMBUSTION ENGINE
...DERS AND 6 HORSE POWER
...petroleum for its reduce free
...ECHANICAL carriage
...the comfortable speed of
MILES PER HOUR
...el, while hills can be ascended
...attended in safety

The Daimler Wagonette
is admirably suited to the needs of the
◄(SPORTSMAN)►
AND LOVER OF THE COUNTRYSIDE,
giving as it does full facilities for
the enjoyment of
FRESH AIR AND AN
UNINTERRUPTED VIEW OF THE Scenery

TWIN-CYLINDER 6 H.P. WAGONETTE (See Engraving)

chassis and machinery, and MMC the coachwork, with the make of the finished car a matter of company whim. As one former MMC employee recalled: 'The Motor Manufacturing Company was in the main mill building; Daimler was in a shed round the back'.

Initially, production was centred on a 4 hp twin; two early publicity stunts which brought the model to the public notice were an ascent of Malvern Beacon and the first motor-car run from John O'Groats to Land's End. At the tiller on the 929-mile journey was J. J. Henry Sturmey, editor of *The Autocar*, which was at that time the official mouthpiece of the Lawson empire. Running time was $93\frac{1}{2}$ hours, and during the

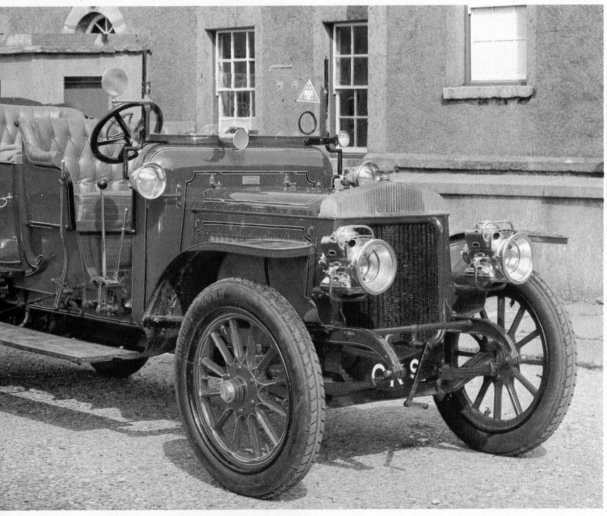

Far left: one of the very first Daimlers, a 4 hp twin-cylinder of 1897. Although the cars were marketed as British Daimlers, all vehicles sold in the company's first few years of production were, in fact, imported from Daimler's namesake in Germany

Above left: The Great Horseless Carriage Company Ltd, which shared premises, products and owner with Daimler, took great pleasure in announcing the 6 hp Wagonette, which had a top speed of 12 mph, albeit on level ground!

Near left: a 1908 tourer beautifully restored, and resplendent in fire-engine red with black and gold pinstriping

Below left: a 1910 Barker-bodied Daimler. Note the ornate beading around the edges of the passenger compartment

trip Sturmey handed out publicity cards to the wondering populace who were near at hand.

Once the marque got under way, a bewildering variety of different models was turned out under the aegis of their works manager, J. S. Critchley; the multitudinous types built over the next five years included $4\frac{1}{2}$, 6, 7, 8, 9 and 11 hp twin-cylinder models and 12, 14, 18, 22 and 24 hp fours. Then, in mid 1902, Daimler ditched this complicated line-up in favour of a three-model range designed by Edmund Lewis. One of the first customers for the new 22 hp model was Edward VII, whose enthusiasm for the marque dated back to 1900, when he had bought a 6 hp Hooper-bodied phaeton, marking the start of a long period of Royal patronage for Daimler.

Possibly because of its Royal connections—the list of customers read like an abridged Debrett—Daimler escaped the spectacular collapse of the Lawson empire in the early 1900s (although the company was reformed

485

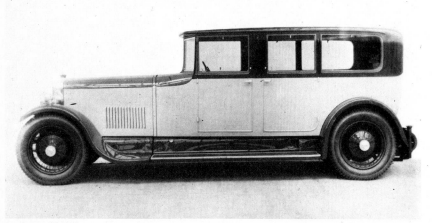

Top: a 1928 Double Six 50 hp limousine

Centre: aggressive and purposeful, a special low-bodied, 1931 Double Six sports car. The name was later used on the Daimler XJ12 versions of the 1970s

Above: the DB 18 of 1935 and, *left,* its 2500 cc, six-cylinder engine

in 1904) and acquired that part of the Motor Mills that had been occupied by MMC. Around this time, too, the distinctive finning on the radiator made its appearance.

Those early Daimlers were noted for their high (by the standards of the day) performance, and the works entered cars in hill-climbs and competitions such as the Kaiserpreis and the Herkomer Trophy—without conspicuous success. A team of three cars ran in the 1907 Targa Florio, entered by the Societa Anonima Officine de Luca Daimler, which built Daimlers under licence in Naples from 1906–1908; despite such star names as Victor Héméry (ex-Darracq) and Hubert Le Blon (ex-Serpollet) alongside works tester George Ison, the team could achieve no better than 13th, 20th and 26th places. Four-cylinder and six-cylinder models of 3.3 litres to 10.4 litres were produced during this period, but in 1908 the company began to switch emphasis from performance to refinement.

The reason was the acquisition of the manufacturing rights to the Knight sleeve-valve engine designed by Charles Yale Knight of Wisconsin. Development of the new power unit was carried out under the supervision of Dr Frederick Lanchester.

At first, both sleeve-valve and poppet-valve engines were built; then the sleeve-valve became standard power for Daimlers, creating the prestige image of the marque—tall, stately cars with a dated appearance, going about their business in silence and a faint haze of oil smoke.

In 1910 came a merger with the Birmingham Small Arms Company, which resulted in some rationalisation of the Daimler and BSA car ranges; and an early benefit of the amalgamation was the development of all-metal construction for some of the group's car bodies.

Munitions, military vehicles and aeroplanes formed the mainstay of the Daimler company's war work in the 1914–18 period; one interesting spin-off was the use of 105 hp Daimler engines in the first tanks.

Post-war car production was centred on three models, launched at the November 1919 Olympia Motor Show: these consisted of two 30 hp types and a 'special' 45 hp model. All had engine lubrication interconnected with the throttle: the oil troughs supplying the big-end bearings were raised by the throttle, so that the faster the unit ran, the more lubrication there was.

The marque's silence earned it a place in broadcasting history in 1922, when the Marconiphone Company used Daimler cars for experiments in wireless reception, although the concept of a receiver that could be used to pick up radio programmes while the car was in motion did not catch on for another decade.

Behind the somewhat dated facade of the finned radiator, Daimler hid some advanced engineering developments: four-wheel-brakes became standard in 1924, as did thinner, lighter, steel sleeve valves for the engine, which resulted in greater power outputs. However, such progress was seemingly wasted on George V, who that year replaced his fleet of 1910 Daimlers with four brand-new 57 hp models which looked almost as dated as their predecessors.

In fact, the 57 hp engines only lasted a couple of years, for in 1926 they were replaced with the company's sensational—and complex—new Double-Six power unit, a 7136 cc sleeve-valve V12, designed by the company's Chief Engineer (and later Managing Director), Laurence Pomeroy.

In 1931, the King acquired a new fleet of Double-Six 50 hp cars, which were mainly notable for the poor proportions of their coachwork. That Daimlers did not

Top: a 1935 limousine in typical Daimler surroundings

Centre: the 1947 DF 36 straight-8 saloon. Note the slightly rounded radiator grill

Above: the DI 253 of 1956 and, *right*, its elegant fascia with the automatic gear selector protruding from the dashboard

have to be fitted with ugly bodies was proved by the activities of various enthusiasts in the early 1930s. Reid Railton collaborated in the production of two lowered-chassis Double-Sixes by Thomson and Taylor of Brooklands for two discerning customers, Captain Wilson and Mr Hutchinson; the first was an open sports four-seater, the second a Weymann coupé. Joseph Mackle, a partner in the London agents for the marque, Stratton-Instone Ltd, won many coachwork competitions with his specially-bodied Daimlers, like the 1929 Magic Carpet, with aerofoil-section running boards, or the Light Straight-Eight of the 1930s, which had raked wings and outside exhaust pipes *à la* Mercedes.

In 1930, Pomeroy was responsible for the fluid-flywheel transmission, which used the Föttinger coupling (originally used for driving the propellors of warships) in conjunction with a conventional cone clutch and crash gearbox to simplify gear changing. Then, Percy Martin, the company chairman, suggested the combination of the fluid flywheel with the Wilson preselector gearbox. This transmission, which became standard on all Daimler, BSA and Lanchester (acquired in 1931) cars, eliminated the clutch, and gave an ease of control which was unrivalled until the introduction of automatics.

As the fluid flywheel came in, though, the Knight engine was on its way out. Technological developments had eliminated the sleeve-valve unit's former superiority in terms of silence, and its extra complication was no longer economically justifiable.

It had a worthy successor in the shape of Pomeroy's second great engine design for the company, the 4.6-litre ohv straight-eight of 1935, based on the 1934 sleeve-valve unit. The 3.4-litre 'Light Straight-Eight' of 1936 was a sign of the changing social climate, for it was 'designed especially for the owner-driver'. The large car range of the mid 1930s was completed by three sizes of straight-six, although a few ohv Double-Six cars were built for prestige purposes. Towards the end of the decade, coil-spring independent front suspension was introduced on Daimler and Lanchester cars, which become virtually badge-engineered twins.

In 1937, Daimler moved out of the Coventry works centred on the old Motor Mills, concentrating production on their Radford Works, acquired in 1908, and progressively enlarged over the years. The Motor Mills survived the move by only a few years; they became an Air Ministry store and were completely gutted during the blitz of Coventry.

Four-wheel-drive scout cars and armoured cars, aero-engines and smaller munitions were the company's main war production. When peace came, the Daimler car range was based on four pre-war models: the DE 27 had a 4.1-litre six-cylinder engine, the DB 18 was a 2.5-litre six, the Straight Eight was enlarged to 5.5 litres and the once-proud name of Lanchester was carried on a 1.3-litre 10 hp model. The DB 18 was the basis of two special versions from Daimler's coachbuilding subsidiaries, Barker (whose Special Sports Coupé was current from March 1949 to July 1952) and Hooper (who made the 'razor-edge' Empress Mark I Saloon, succeeded in 1952 by the Mark 2, with aluminium cylinder head, preselector gearbox and overdrive). A 3-litre, six-cylinder engine was announced in late 1951 and a four-cylinder variant was used in a new Lanchester 14, which became the basis for the Daimler Conquest of 1953.

For a time, Daimler concentrated production on medium-sized cars, phasing out the DE 27 in July 1951 and the Straight-Eight in November 1953; but the 3-litre Regency proved to be underpowered and

Top: Daimler entered a completely new field with the glassfibre-bodied SP 250 sports cars

Above: Daimler V8 2½-litre saloon

was upgraded to 3.5 litres as the Regency Mk 2.

A performance version of the Conquest appeared in 1954, fitted with an aluminium cylinder head and twin carburettors to boost power output from 75 to 100 bhp. This Conquest Century survived until January 1958, by which time Borg-Warner automatic transmission was offered as an alternative to the preselector gear. This was the choice, too, on the 3.5 litre 104; but when this model was replaced by the 3.8 litre Majestic in 1958, only the Borg-Warner was available.

Lanchester had been killed off in 1956, and in 1960 Daimler was bought by the buoyant Jaguar Car Company, which was urgently seeking room to expand. Apart from the more specialised versions such as the 1960 4.5-litre V8 Majestic Major and its stretched Limousine variant, and the glassfibre-bodied SP 250 sports car, designed by Edward Turner (Ogle design studies to improve the looks of this car became, somehow, the Reliant Scimitar), most Daimlers were based on the contemporary Jaguar models from that time on. Power, however, was provided by the pre-merger 2.5-litre and 4.5-litre V8 engines.

Externally, only vestigial fluting on the dummy radiator shell distinguishes the later Daimlers from their raffish younger sisters, the range being centred on the newest version of the Sovereign range. The Sovereign of 1973 had the Jaguar V12 power unit and predictably, the Double-Six name was revived for this model.
DBW

Above: 43 years of Double Six: 1931 and 1974 vintage

Left: the Series Two Sovereign V12 of 5.3 litres

DAIMLER LIMOUSINE

Introduced in 1968 by Daimler of Great Britain, the Limousine has a Jaguar 4.2-litre XK engine clothed in a Vanden Plas body. In 1974, a new Landaulette version of the car was announced, having a convertible rear compartment. By 1974, these were the only Daimler models not duplicated by Jagu-'ar, despite the use of Jaguar engines and running gear.

The engine has a long and distinguished pedigree, having powered five Le Mans-winning cars. It is a straight-six with twin overhead camshafts and twin two-inch SU carburettors. Power output from this large but low-compression engine is 162 bhp (DIN), while there is plenty of torque, at 230 lb ft, to accelerate this two-ton car at a considerable rate.

A Borg-Warner model 12 automatic gearbox is a standard fitting; in fact there is no manual gearbox available. This three-speed unit drives the rear wheels via a propeller shaft and a hypoid-bevel final drive.

Suspension is Jaguar. At the front, there are two semi-trailing wishbones, coil-spring telescopic-damper units and an anti-roll bar, while the rear has a lower transverse link, a longitudinal radius arm and a fixed-length half-shaft, suspended by twin coil-spring/damper units each side. These suspension arrangements have been used by Jaguar for many years on both road and track and have met with great success.

Disc brakes are used all round, the rear ones being mounted inboard, adjacent to the differential. Servo assistance is provided and the handbrake, which operates on the rear wheels, is self adjusting.

The power-assisted steering mechanism is of the somewhat outmoded recirculating-ball type, but is light and effective. The steering wheel is adjustable for reach by loosening a nurled ring round the column.

The four-door Vanden Plas body is luxuriously furnished, especially in the Landaulette, and the car is really aimed at the person who can afford not only the purchase price (each Landaulette is built to personal preference), but a chauffeur to fill the imposing front compartment.

ENGINE Front-mounted, in-line 6, water cooled. 92.1 mm (3.63 in) bore × 106 mm (4.17 in) stroke = 4235 cc (258 cu in). Maximum power 162 bhp (DIN) at 4250 rpm; maximum torque 230 lb ft (DIN) at 3000 rpm; maximum engine rpm 5500. Cast-iron cylinder block, light-alloy head; compression ratio 7.5:1; 7 main bearings. 2 valves per cylinder operated by 2 chain-driven overhead camshafts. 2 SU sidedraught carburettors.

TRANSMISSION Borg Warner torque converter (maximum ratio at stall 2:1) and model 12 3-speed automatic gearbox with planetary gears (ratios 1st 2.4, 2nd 1.45, 3rd 1.0, reverse 2.0:1); with a hypoid-bevel final drive (ratio 3.54:1) driving the rear wheels.

CHASSIS Monocoque body/chassis.

SUSPENSION Front—independent by semi-trailing unequal-length wishbones, coil springs, telescopic dampers and anti-roll bar; rear—independent by lower transverse links, longitudinal arms, fixed-length drive shafts, coil springs and telescopic dampers.

STEERING Recirculating ball, power assisted; 2.75 turns from lock to lock.

BRAKES Hydraulic discs front and rear, with servo assistance; swept area 234 sq in front and 212 sq in rear; self-adjusting handbrake operating on rear wheels.

WHEELS 6 in × 15 pressed steel.

TYRES 205 × 15.

DIMENSIONS AND WEIGHT Wheelbase 141 in; track 58 in front and rear; length 226 in; width 77½ in; height 63¾ in; ground clearance 7 in; kerb weight 4700 lb; turning circle between walls 46 ft; fuel tank 20 gals.

BODY Saloon; 4 doors; 8 seats (Landaulette body available, with convertible rear compartment); glass partition between driver and passenger compartments.

PERFORMANCE Speeds in the gears—1st 48 mph, 2nd 79 mph, 3rd 115 mph; acceleration—standing ¼-mile 19 secs; fuel consumption 14–16 mpg.

SMOOTHING OUT THE BUMPS

Most people know the term 'shock absorber', but few realise that this description, though widespread, is really a misnomer

Above: a coil-spring/ telescopic-damper unit in use on a Formula Atlantic racing car. This type of assembly is popular on road cars as well as on the vast majority of racing machinery

Right: four types of damper which have been used over the years. The ribbon damper consisted of a ribbon wrapped round and fixed at one end to a sprung pulley (rather like a tape measure) which was stiff to turn. The other end of the ribbon was connected to the suspension, thus giving damping on bump or rebound, depending on the point of connection. The friction damper was slightly later and gave two-way damping, but was not reliable or efficient. The rotary-vane damper was an early type of hydraulic unit, incorporating a two-vaned rotor which turned and moved fluid from one side of a partition to the other. The only difference between this and the lever damper is that the latter uses a normal piston

DEFLECT A SPRING and then release it; it will spring back past its original position and go on oscillating for some time, each swing being of smaller amplitude than the one before yet taking the same amount of time. The only thing that stops the oscillation from continuing undisturbed is hysteresis: the loss of energy internally through a kind of molecular friction in the structure of the spring material. A well made steel spring has low hysteresis so, when a car bounces on its springs on riding a bump, the bouncing will continue for some time afterwards. This could be dangerous and is at least disconcerting, so some means of ensuring the necessary hysteresis, or energy loss, in the system must be provided. The quality of the spring material must not be debased, so the means must be external to the spring: the damper does the work, checking the free oscillation of the spring by converting the energy stored in the spring into heat.

The damper is not a shock absorber, despite the common misuse of the term. The spring absorbs the shock, converting the force applied in deflecting it into energy stored in its mass; the damper dissipates that energy, converting it into readily dissipated heat. A good one will virtually stop the oscillation of a suspension spring in $1\frac{1}{2}$ cycles of flexure, while the torsional damper on a crankshaft should check any torsional flutter within half a degree of twist. The damper does not have to be anywhere near as strong as the spring, for surprisingly little effort may be needed to alter the frequency of oscillation from what is natural to the spring in question.

Although damping is applied to many car components having natural spring characteristics (such as crankshafts, valve springs, seat upholstery, steering, body panels, fan blades, and dozens more), the best known dampers in a car are those controlling the suspension. Nearly always, but not invariably, they are to be found near each wheel and are hydraulic. Their working principle is based on the observation that if you try to pump a lot of liquid through a tiny hole in a short time you will find it very hard work indeed: the hydraulic damper is essentially a pump in which the working fluid (oil) is forced through a small hole, or holes. The resistance of the fluid to passage through a hole becomes greater as the rate of pumping is increased, so the sharp and profound spring deflection caused by the wheel hitting a big bump at high speed will require, and get, more damping action than the gentle flexure of the spring when the wheel is rolling slowly on a smooth road.

This convenient property was not shared by the friction dampers which were in general use until the late 1930s (though the racing Mors had hydraulic dampers in 1902). These offered more resistance to spring motion when the spring was still than when it was oscillating. Various methods of varying the pressure between their friction plates were tried in attempts to improve their behaviour by reducing the

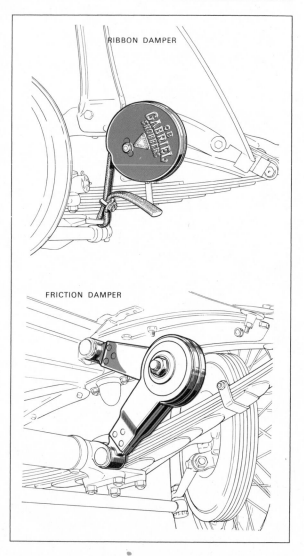

RIBBON DAMPER

FRICTION DAMPER

'stiction' or binding of the stationary plates: this culminated in the very costly, complicated and sensitive de Ram dampers most notably to be seen on some late Bugattis. Most of these methods relied on hydraulic control, so it was natural to rely on hydraulics entirely, and this became universal practice in the '50s.

Most early hydraulic dampers were linked by levers to the axle or hub carrier, the lever imparting a rotary motion to a spindle carrying a vane which pumped the fluid from one side of an internal partition to the other. Gradually, this rotary vane type (and the intermediate lever type which contained pistons in hydraulic cylinders) gave way to the telescopic damper, which is most popular today. The telescopic damper has two advantages: one is that its linear action accurately reproduces the amplitude and velocity of wheel movement (provided, as is not always the case, that it is appropriately located), the other is that it has a high ratio of surface area to volume and can therefore shed its heat more easily. Both these factors make the telescopic type more consistent and less sensitive to extraneous influences, while internally more sensitive to adjustment.

The heyday of development for this type of damper was the 1960s. Special formulations were then developed for the working fluid, based on silicone anti-foaming agents invented in the 1940s. Foaming or aeration is inimical to damping efficiency, for the bubbles of entrained air reduce the apparent viscosity of the fluid so that it can more readily be squirted

action: the pressurised gas merely controls the working fluid and replaces the old recuperation chamber which used to contain air.

There are three kinds of valve or hole through which the oil may be forced when the damper operates. One is the orifice, a plain hole of modest diameter, another is the bleed, a small hole, or holes, often arranged to act as a by-pass for certain working conditions and, thirdly, there is the blow-off valve, spring-loaded to remain closed until the pressure and rate of flow overcome the spring. Most telescopic dampers embody all three types, some only two. They are located in the piston of the moving member and at the foot of the

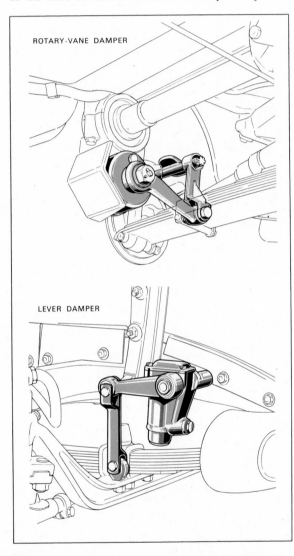

ROTARY-VANE DAMPER

LEVER DAMPER

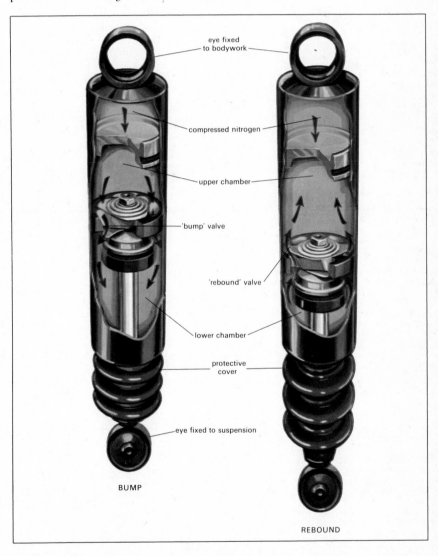

eye fixed to bodywork

compressed nitrogen

upper chamber

'bump' valve

'rebound' valve

lower chamber

protective cover

eye fixed to suspension

BUMP

REBOUND

through the orifices which control its rate of flow. For similar reasons, the oil must have a high viscosity index (that is, a low rate of change of viscosity with temperature) or it will be too sensitive to heat. Damper fade, caused by heat and aeration, was a frequent problem in high-performance cars of the early 1950s.

A variety of means are adopted to combat these effects. In some dampers, the fluid is always circulated in one direction, returning by a parallel route and being cooled on the way. In others, the vacant space necessarily left inside the damper, when the correct amount of fluid has been inserted, is filled by a closed-cell plastics sacs which expand to take up space. Another innovation is the use of an inert gas in a pressure chamber separated from the oil by a free piston or an elastic diaphragm. The gas-filled damper does not in any way rely on the gas for its damping

static member, so as to control flow in either direction at any point of the piston stroke. Each type has different characteristics of response to speed and load and, by adjusting the diameter of a hole, multiplying or decreasing the number of holes, and altering the strength of the springs controlling valves, it is possible to achieve hundreds of different settings.

Some types of damper, especially those used in racing, are adjustable by external means. Adjustment may be confined to the rebound stroke only, or extend to the bump stroke as well, and may only affect the damping at high speeds (by altering the blow-off valve setting, for example) or at low, or overall. Dampers electrically controlled by the driver, while the car is in motion, have been produced in the past, but have encountered little welcome other than from Aston Martin, Bristol and Rolls-Royce.   LJKS

Above: two cutaway views of a telescopic damper, showing the movement of the piston through the fluid on bump and rebound. Note how different valves open and close on each stroke, so that the damping factor can be adjusted

DESPITE THE SOUR AFTERTASTE left by Detroit's recent recalls of defective cars, the truth is that cars are actually safer now than ever. Sophisticated design and engineering have made for better handling, stronger tyres, improved braking and more effective shock absorbing devices, such as bumpers and padded dashboards. In short, from a mechanical standpoint, the odds are in favor of today's driver getting from here to there in one piece. Yet, it is estimated that in 1975 fifty thousand people will die on America's highways, and approximately 2 million others will suffer disabling accidents.

Why? If the fundamental answer does not lie with the mechanical frailties of automobiles, then we may assume that it lies with the human frailties of the people who drive them. This, indeed, has been borne out by the latest researches into the causes of motor vehicle accidents. According to these studies, the greater an individual's psychological and emotional problems, the more dangerous a driver he or she will be.

Although psychiatrists agree that emotional disturbance and high-powered cars are a bad mix, they differ markedly over which type of disturbed person makes the most dangerous driver. Psychotics, who are undeniably potential killers, aside, psychiatrists' characterizations of the worst bets on the road range from sexual ne'er-do-wells to social anarchists. A UCLA professor holds that bad drivers are 'immature bullies covering up their sexual inadequacies,' while an East Coast expert zeroes in more closely on this proposition, remarking that 'hot rod addicts use their cars as proof of their masculinity and often as actual substitutes for women.' Though unfortunately he neglects to expand on the fascinating last part of his statement.

Another investigator casts a wider net, contending that the most dangerous driver is an 'egotical, impulsive exhibitionist, lacking responsibility and rejecting authority.'

Learned opinions of this sort, combined with our nationwide accident statistics, tend to conjure up a terrifying picture of highways filled with wildly careening lunatics, bent on murder and mayhem. Granted that many accidents are psychologically based, the overiding fact emerging from the studies is that those who cause them are not psychotics or even neurotics, but are simply people who may be under momentary psychological stress. The man who has had a fight with his boss, for instance, is more likely to have an accident than one driving home after a routine day's work. Similarly, the woman who has just quarreled with her husband stands a better chance of racking up the family car on her way to the supermarket than the wife who sallies forth to do her shopping in a state of marital bliss.

While most of us are prone to occasional 'blue' moods, and are potentially dangerous drivers during those periods, certain specific groups within the general population appear to be consistently more dangerous than others. Thus, the studies tell us—to the obvious delight of Fem Libbers—men cause more accidents than women, and adolescent males are, this side of madmen, unquestionably the worst offenders of all the groupings.

The dismal statistical showings of males seem to be rooted in society's standards of masculine behaviour, on the one hand, and in the shrinking outlets for that behaviour on the other. Many men have been taught since childhood that it is desireable to meet challenges, behave aggressively, find new enterprises and take risks. At the same time, our freewheeling frontier days, in which *machismo* was at a premium, are long

DO YOU DRIVE DANGEROUSLY?

What constitutes dangerous driving? Although there are some hard-and-fast rules, the answer depends on circumstances

past. The upshot is that many men, feeling trapped by routine jobs and a regimented life, resort to high risk activities to reassure their masculinity. Fast skiing is one—but so is hell-for-leather driving.

The problem in the adolescent male is still more complicated, with the result that he often literally becomes a 'wildman' behind the wheel. Raised, like his father, to revere aggressive masculine traits, he adds to these the rebellious characteristics of puberty. Dr. Frederick McGuire, professor of psychiatry at the California College of Medicine, feels that teenagers may be more apt to have accidents, because in trying to define their status and find themselves, they may look for safety rules to break as a way of lashing out against authroty.

Cultural expectations have also left their mark on our female drivers, and the age-old convention that holds women to be the 'gentle sex' is corroborated on the highway, in contradiction to the equally persistent belief that women are terrible drivers. Surprisingly, researchers found the most sure-handed of all American motorists to be women from sixteen to twenty-five. Whether this will change as women move rapidly into traditional male roles is anybody's guess, and a frightening one at that.

Psychiatrists probing the causes of dangerous driving have forcefully made their point about the importance of the psychological/emotional factors involved. It remains for legislators to recognize these factors in laws which provide for tests to weed out psychotics and other deeply disturbed individuals, who are certifiably unfit to handle motor vehicles. This, at least, would provide a measure of protection against the most likely potential killers. As for the rest of us, the best we can do is try to avoid the driver's seat when we feel angry or depressed and, whenever we are in it, keep a sharp eye on the other fellow—especially if he looks like a teenager.   JH

Above: the driver of this Ford Escort Mexico has spun his car while taking a corner at high speed in the rain at the Brands Hatch race track. The race circuits are, in fact, about the only place that drivers can legally break most of the rules of public-road safety, but even then it's not so safe, as our picture shows. However, even race tracks are governed by a strict set of rules which, like road safety regulations, are subject to conditions and circumstances

A MOTOR ENTHUSIAST WHO HATED DRIVING

Alexandre Darracq was a man with a great passion for engineering and motor racing.
Incredibly he hated riding in cars and was an extremely poor driver himself!

ALEXANDRE DARRACQ WAS, it was said, an engineer 'by temperament if not by qualification'. Born in 1855, he worked first in an arsenal, then at the Hurtu factory, manufacturing sewing machines. However, although a machine of Darracq's design won him a gold medal at the 1889 Paris exhibition, his natural instincts were those of a sharp financier rather than a mechanic. He was soon enjoying the bicycle boom, making cycles in a workshop in the Place de la Nation. Later, an association with a new partner, Jean Aucoc, led to a diversion into vintner's sundries, then to the establishment of a factory in the Pré-Saint-Gervais, making Gladiator bicycles, which soon established an enviable track record, breaking records and winning races in Europe and America.

Hardly surprisingly, the company came into the orbit of that notorious entrepreneur, Adolphe Clément, and was one of the three companies involved in the 22 million franc flotation of the Clément-Gladiator-Humber consortium. Darracq was bought out on condition that he didn't set up as a cycle manufacturer again; so he built cycle components instead, and dodged the terms of the contract.

A brand-new factory was built at Suresnes, and a start in motor-cycle manufacture was made with the odd five-cylinder, rotary-engined Millet; but more orthodox devices soon prevailed. Darracq saw that there was a profit to be made in the horseless carriage, and moved in with an electric brougham, following with a Leon Bollée-designed voiturette. The success of Bollée's three-wheeler seemed to guarantee that the £10,000 that Darracq paid for the manufacturing rights of this latest design was money well spent. Unfortunately, the little four-wheeler was a flop, even by the uncritical standards of 1898. Its five-speed belt-drive was a masterpiece of bad design, and the obsolete hot-tube ignition added to the problems.

Once it was running, the curious steering layout promised early disaster.

Fortunately, Darracq soon hired another designer, Ribeyrolles, who had more orthodox ideas on car layout and conceived a handsome 6.5 hp *voiture légère* with a front-mounted 785 cc, single-cylinder engine, a shaft and bevel-driven rear axle, and a three-speed steering column gear change. The model was intended for mass-production, and, although demand never reached the heady heights dreamed of by Darracq, it did sell by the hundred, and was also built under licence in Germany by Opel.

By 1903, the range had grown to four cars: a 1.1-litre single, 1.3 and 1.9-litre twins and a 3.8-litre four. The following year, all the multi-cylinder models had acquired pressed-steel frames instead of the flitch-plated wood chassis of the earlier model. There was also a new 'Flying Fifteen' 3-litre four, whose frame, pressed from a single sheet of steel, was a masterpiece of metal forming.

During this period, the marque's name was being kept in the sporting public's eye by a series of extravagantly-lightened racing *voitures légères* while, in 1904, Alexandre Darracq, who was renowned for the fact that he never missed a trick, tried to win the Gordon Bennett Trophy by sheer brute force, entering teams of identical cars built in Britain, France and Germany. However, the 11.3-litre monsters failed miserably.

Far more successful was the 1905 200 hp V8 sprint car, which used two Gordon Bennett-type cylinder blocks with overhead valve gear on a common crankcase; it was capable of virtually 120 mph and was one

Above left: now preserved in the Turin Automobile Museum, this Darracq used a single-cylinder, 1281 cc engine, producing 9 bhp at 1200 rpm

Above right: a 1902 Darracq. Until that year, all models had been fitted with single-cylinder engines, save for the racing voiturette versions, which used 5.4-litre, four-cylinder motors

of the two fastest cars in the world.

Alexandre Darracq's enthusiasm for motor sport was all the more remarkable because, though he was said to have taken driving lessons in July 1896, he apparently hated riding in cars.

The marque's great racing days ended in 1906 with Louis Wagner's second victory in the American Vanderbilt Cup, driving a 12.7-litre racer. After that, all was anti-climax, and Wagner joined the Fiat team in 1907. One final race, the 1908 'Four-Inch' Isle of Man Tourist Trophy, in which the team took second, third and seventh places, closed the record as far as the factory was concerned, though Malcolm Campbell raced ex-works Darracqs at Brooklands in 1912.

In any case, Darracq had found a new enthusiasm— or, at least, a new source of profits—in the infant sport of aviation, sending a journalist named Fordyce to America in 1907 to bargain for the Wright Brothers' patents. A couple of years later, the Suresnes factory began production of a light aero-engine which was used by such intrepid birdmen as Blériot and Santos-Dumont. For the time being, the company's aeronautical activities remained a sideline, though they assumed a more serious aspect during World War I.

Another peripheral activity proved more costly for, in 1906, Darracq signed an agreement with Serpollet, planning to flood the capitals of Europe with fleets of steam buses. The flood was never more than a trickle, with only a few dozen buses ever going into service— 20 ran in London—and the company suffered a loss.

A further disaster had a major impact on motoring history. In 1906, a factory had been set up in Milan to build Darracqs for the Italian market, but the cars failed to sell in sufficient numbers and, by 1910, the Societa Italiana Automobili Darracq was out of business. In its place came the Anonima Lombardo Fabbrica Automobili; ALFA was taken over by Nicola Romeo in 1914, and Alfa Romeo was born.

By 1911, it looked as though Alexandre Darracq was back on course again. He had proposed, as early as 1898, to build cars that combined quality and low cost, by making use of the economies that could be achieved by series production. True, he had just killed off the last of the old, ultra-cheap, single-cylinder models, and the twins had only a few months to run, but a new 14–16 hp model costing only £260 in Britain seemed to augur well for the marque's future.

However, Alexandre Darracq was about to invoke his personal Nemesis again. After much unaccountable juggling with the range, he announced, in 1912, that most of the line-up would be graced with the Henriod rotary-valve engine, which featured a single port for each cylinder performing as inlet or exhaust depending on the position of the rotating valve shaft. Early rotary-valve Darracqs had a dashboard radiator à la Renault, but a redesign of the valve gear permitted the use of a conventional cooler. The Henriod-powered models ranged from 2.1 to 3.6 litres and all were completely gutless, as well as being liable to seize up.

Profits—and the marque's reputation—plummeted, and Alexandre Darracq resigned. He died in 1931. The firm was placed under the control of a Yorkshireman, Owen Clegg, who had designed the very successful Rover Twelve. Not being one to change a winning formula in the face of a crisis, Clegg based the new Darracq on the Rover; the Henriod was immediately chopped, and the Suresnes works completely re-equipped for mass-production. The 16 hp Clegg-Darracq had an engine of just under 3 litres, and was soon joined by a 2.1-litre, 12 hp model; both were handsome, well-proportioned, reliable cars and, within months, production had risen to 60 cars a week. By the

autumn of 1914, 12,000 men were working at Suresnes, turning out 14 chassis daily. The 16 hp, anglicised still further, was the leading post-Armistice model, but was soon joined by a 4.6-litre V8 with four forward speeds and—from the end of 1920—four-wheel braking as well. For all its advanced specification, the new car proved a disappointment, and was gently phased out over the next three or four years. By that time also, A. Darracq & Co Ltd (the company had been re-registered in England in 1903 to dodge French fiscal law) had ceased to exist. In October 1919, they had acquired Clément-Talbot of London, only to be themselves swallowed up by Sunbeam.

Though the Darracq name survived on those of the Sunbeam-Talbot-Darracq group's products destined for Britain or its Empire, it was no more than a very convoluted exercise in badge-engineering, and the latter history of the cars from Suresnes must be told in due course, as a part of the Sunbeam and Talbot stories.   DBW

Top: the 8/10 hp model of 1908 used an 1100 cc, single-cylinder engine, employing mechanically operated valves. The car sold for around £160 in Britain

Above: the 1912 Darracq model range was fitted with the four-cylinder Henriod rotary-valve engine. The engine, hopelessly underpowered, was prone to seizure and was responsible for the ruination of Darracq's hitherto excellent reputation

POWERFUL CHALLENGER FROM THE EAST

After World War II, Japan's motor industry was in ruins. Today, Datsun is the world's fourth-largest car producer. Its recovery is nothing short of a miracle

COMPARED WITH THE GREAT European car manufacturers, the main Japanese firms are very young. Nissan-Datsun, now the fourth largest car manufacturer in the world, can trace its ancestry back only to the early 1930s, when three Japanese financiers—Den, Aoyama and Takeuchi—formed a car company called Kai Shinsha Motors. The cars it made took their name from the initials of the three backers: D.A.T. The idea was to promote the car as the son of the three gentlemen—hence DATSON. But 'son' is also the Japanese for 'loss', and the result was a hasty change to DATSUN.

In 1933, the company was established on a new basis with a public shareholding; the change of name to Nissan Motor Company followed in 1934. By 1935, it had set up a Ford-type production line and was already exporting. Among its first products was a car owing a good deal to the Austin Seven.

Although set for apparent growth, Nissan fell under the shadow of the approaching war. By 1938, passenger-car production was restricted and the Yokohama fac-

tory was concentrating on building army trucks. At the end of the war, in common with most of Japanese industry, Nissan lay in ruins. The occupation forces took over the factories and, in the immediate post-war period, production consisted entirely of trucks for their use.

In 1947, though, car production was resumed on a modest scale. The first models were again British-based, derived from the then-current Austin models, and this was to set the pattern right through to the early 1950s. By this time, Nissan's cars closely resembled the Austin Devon and Somerset, but the firm was busy on designs of its own. By 1955, they were ready to go into production.

In that same year, the occupation forces finally relinquished their hold on all Nissan's factories, enabling the Japanese to organise production properly. The Datsun 110 saloon and 120 pickup truck (derived from it) began to appear in some numbers. The 110 started a long line of development which can be traced right through to the 1974 Bluebirds though, at that

Above: Datsun's 2393 cc, six-cylinder 240Z has established itself as the world's best-selling sports car. Its low-speed torque, good roadholding and high top speed have also made it a highly competitive rally car. Pictured above is a 240Z competing in the 1972 Monte Carlo Rally in the capable hands of Finland's Rauno Aaltonen

495

This page, from top to bottom

The 25 bhp Datsun 113 sedan. This 850 cc machine was the first Datsun to be put onto the world market

A Datsun 1600SSS sweeps to victory in the gruelling 1970 East African Safari Rally

Equally at home in the Alps and on the rally routes of Africa, a 1970 Datsun 1200

On opposite page, from top to bottom
By 1972, Datsun had established themselves in Britain. This is the 180B SSS model

The 1973 200L saloon, Datsun's competitive entry in the middle-size saloon market

The highly popular 120A model features unusual three-door, fastback styling

Datsun's 1974 120Y, showing the distinctive side-view styling known in the trade as the 'Coke bottle' style

time, the name had not been adopted.

By 1958, standards were high enough, and production large enough, for Nissan to enter the American market, concentrating on California where the cars were first shown. Before long, a nation-wide sales network had been set up. In 1959, it was able to offer Americans the new Datsun 310, now named Bluebird and, in the following year, the first Datsun 2000 (also to found an unbroken line of successors) appeared.

Production and exports continued to grow, based largely on the Bluebird. In 1961, Nissan became Japan's top car exporter, and was planning great increases in production capacity as well as new models. The purpose-built Oppama plant, on the edge of Tokyo bay, south of Yokohama, went into operation in 1962. Next year, two notable landmarks were passed—the Bluebird topped 200,000 units, and exports reached 100,000.

From this point on, expansion was very rapid. The 1964 production rate for the Bluebird exceeded 10,000 cars a month; the first time a Japanese manufacturer had built a single model at such a high rate. The Oppama plant was proving its worth, and the next project—the Zama plant, west of Tokyo—was rising from green fields. Intended at first as a truck factory, it was soon turned over to car production as demand increased.

Nissan was now definitely heading for a place in the 'big league'. Its model range was not wide enough, so it produced the big President, a genuine prestige car, still, in 1974, sold only in Japan, and replaced the 2000 with a new model. At the same time, the firm began to build up a fleet of specialised car carriers, primarily to take cars to America.

In 1966, the model range was expanded in the other direction with the introduction of the Datsun 1000. This small, modern four-seater set a new pattern, offering a chance of 'proper' motoring to the not-so-well-off Japanese, who had previously been offered only a choice of several 360 cc minicars. While this was a move in the Japanese domestic market, Nissan also launched a campaign for world-wide recognition by entering the world of motor sport. The result was a dramatic success on the 14th East African Safari Rally.

To round off 1966, there came a massive merger. Nissan joined forces with Prince Motors, makers of the Skyline range, and thus inherited not only an extra model line but also a splendid factory and test track at Murayama near Tokyo. At the time, the new combine was Japan's largest car manufacturer, although a subsequent series of mergers resulted in Toyota being larger still. These moves set the final pattern of the Japanese industry, dominated by the two major firms: Nissan–Datsun centred on Tokyo, and Toyota with their factories grouped around Nagoya.

The next years saw steady expansion of production and exports, and the introduction of more new models. Of these, perhaps the most important was the 510 Bluebird, a car which appeared shortly after the Mark 2 Ford Cortina, and was almost exactly the same size (and shape, some thought). However, the Bluebird had an overhead-camshaft engine—in a choice of sizes, 1300 cc and 1600 cc—and independent rear suspension by semi-trailing arms. The same units were used in the 1600 Sport, a two-seater version of which was sent to America in search of a slice of the MGB market.

The new Bluebird formula was repeated in 1968, the following year, with the larger 1800 Laurel. This was the year in which Datsun, having spent some time building itself up in Europe, finally entered the British market with a range of four cars, the 1000, the Bluebird 1300 and 1600, and the 2000.

If the 510 Bluebird proved Nissan's designers capable of modern thinking, the car which dramatically confirmed it was the 240Z. Produced at a time when other manufacturers were saying a new sports car could not be designed because sales would never be enough to pay for the development costs, Nissan aimed the 240Z squarely at the American market, and it was

an instant success. Very soon, it was the world's biggest-selling sports car.

Though advanced in many ways, the 240Z was still a sensible and practical design. Its engine was in effect one-and-a-half Bluebird engines—six cylinders instead of four, but with the same cylinder dimensions and layout. Like the Bluebird, it used MacPherson strut suspension at the front (but, unlike the saloon, had strut suspension at the back, too). Work immediately started on developing the 240Z as a rally car, a programme eventually to result in two more outright wins in the East African Safari.

The development of more mundane cars was not neglected. First, the 1000 was replaced by the 1200, larger, more powerful, and, in some ways (as in the front suspension design), more advanced also. Into the gap beneath the 1200, Nissan introduced the 100A Cherry, a little car which broke new ground in adopting the transverse-engine, front-drive layout pioneered by Alec Issigonis. Strangely, perhaps, the Cherry has not been a great success in Japan, but has found ready acceptance in more sophisticated export markets, most of all in Europe.

Having strengthened the bottom end of the range, Nissan next replaced the ageing 2000 with an entirely new and much improved car, the 240C—which rapidly grew into the 260C. Its engine was a detuned version of that used in the 240Z, and the enlargement of its capacity (by lengthening the stroke rather than boring-out) hinted at developments to come.

In the meantime, even more work was going on to give a new look to the middle of the range, and three more new cars appeared. First and largest was the 200L Laurel, in effect a replacement for the old 1800 and, like it, built at Murayama. The Laurel has an engine derived from the original Prince Motors G-series overhead-camshaft power unit, which was also retained when, later in the same year, the Skyline range was completely overhauled. Almost simultaneously, the Oppama factory began to build the series 610, known as the Bluebird 'U' to the Japanese, to distinguish it from the 510, which they kept in production. The 610, though designed along the same lines as the 510 and in effect a progressive development of it, was bigger and more expensive; the 510 had to wait another year for a direct replacement in the form of the series 710 Violet.

In the Violet, the design process came full circle, since the 710 was in most ways a 'shrunken 610'. Nissan thus had, in the most important area of all, two closely-related designs with all the advantages of many common spare parts and fewer service problems. Both the 610 and 710 were designed with safety requirements very much in mind, as was the 120Y, introduced to replace the 1200.

The Datsun range, early in 1974, therefore consisted of the 100A Cherry at the bottom, working up through the 120Y Sunny and 140J Violet (also built with a bigger engine as the 160J). Then came the 160B/180B Bluebird, recently extended to include a 2-litre, six-cylinder version; the 200L Laurel; the Skyline range (all the way from the basic 160K to the longer-wheelbase, six-cylinder 240K GT sports saloon). The largest mass-produced model was the 200C/260C, though the even larger President—with 3-litre straight-six or 4-litre V8—was produced in fair numbers. Nor must one forget the 260Z (as the 240Z has become) and its long-wheelbase, two-plus-two version.

That Datsun could start afresh from the ashes of World War II is remarkable, but that they could, in just over thirty years, be a world force is nothing short of a miracle.   JD

DATSUN 260Z

Not long after the Datsun 240Z was unveiled at the 1969 Tokyo motor show, it established itself as one of the world's best-selling sports cars.

The car's biggest market was America (130,000 of the 153,000 240Zs exported over a 3½-year period between 1970 and 1973 were sold in the USA) where the car was looked on, somewhat unfairly, as a successor to the much-mourned Austin Healey 3000. Admittedly, the 240Z's 2.4-litre, straight-six engine was in the same mould as that of the old Healey: plenty of low-speed torque for effortless acceleration.

Then, Datsun announced a 2.6-litre version of the 240Z, the 260Z, with a power output of 162 bhp and maximum torque of 152 lb ft as opposed to 151 bhp and 146 lb ft, respectively, for the older car. The new model retained many of the features of the 240Z including its rugged looks and its five-speed gearbox, albeit suitably modified to cope with the extra power and higher ratios for both first and second gears.

Although the 260Z has a neat, three-door body with plenty of room for two people and all their luggage, Datsun has had a great demand for a 2 + 2 seater. So, at the 1973 Tokyo show, they launched the 260Z 2+2; the wheelbase being lengthened by 11.9 inches to accommodate the extra seats. The 2+2, as with many Japanese cars, has many so-called optional extras as standard equipment such as tinted glass, reclining front seats with built-in head restraints and a radio and eight-track-tape stereo system.

Both the 260 models have a top speed of 127 mph, accelerate to 60 mph in just over 8 seconds and return an average fuel consumption of just on 25 mpg.

The 240–260s have not only asserted themselves as fine road-going sports cars but as serious competition cars, their most notable success being an outright victory on the gruelling 1973 East African Safari Rally in the hands of Shekhar Mehta.

ENGINE Front-mounted, water-cooled, in-line 6. 83 mm (3.27 in) bore × 79 mm (3.11 in) stroke = 2565 cc (156.5 cu in). Maximum power 162 bhp (SAE) at 5600 rpm; maximum torque 152 lb ft (SAE) at 4400 rpm. Cast-iron cylinder block and light-alloy head; compression ratio 8.3:1. 7 main bearings. 2 valves per cylinder operated directly by a single, overhead camshaft. 2 Hitachi HJG 46W (SU type) carburettors.

TRANSMISSION Single dry plate clutch; 5-speed all synchromesh gearbox; ratios—1st 2.91, 2nd 1.90, 3rd 1.31, 4th 1.0, 5th 0.86, reverse 3.38; hypoid bevel final drive, ratio 3.70:1 driving rear wheels.

CHASSIS Integral with auxiliary front sub-frame.

SUSPENSION Front—independent by MacPherson struts, lower transverse and drag links, coil springs and anti-roll bar; rear—independent by Chapman Struts with coil springs, telescopic dampers, lower auxiliary arms and fixed-length drive shafts.

STEERING Rack and pinion, ratio 15.8:1. Turns from lock to lock: 2.8.

BRAKES Vacuum servo assisted discs front and drums rear (drums finned on 2+2). Total swept area 393.7 sq in.

WHEELS Pressed-steel disc 5½ in.

TYRES Radial-ply, tubeless 195/70VR14.

DIMENSIONS AND WEIGHT Wheelbase 90.7 in (102.6 in 2+2); track 53.3 in front, 53.0 in rear; length 162.8 in (175.0 in 2 2); width 64.2 in (65.2 in 2+2); height 50.6 in; ground clearance 6.3 in; kerb weight 2425 lb (2557 lb 2+2); turning circle between walls 35 ft; fuel tank capacity 13.2 gals.

BODY Sports coupé 3 doors, 2 or 4 seats.

PERFORMANCE Maximum speed both models 127 mph. Acceleration 0–60 mph approximately 8 seconds. Fuel consumption 25 mpg.

The grand old man of motor racing

NOWADAYS IT IS QUITE A COMMON OCCURRENCE for a racing driver, flushed with success and equipped with a tape recorder and a ghost writer, to make a token attempt at motoring journalism. But for a writer of very real talent to become, in his 30s, a competition driver of international standard must be unique. Yet that is what happened to Sidney Charles Houghton Davis—otherwise known as 'Sammy'—born in London in 1887 and educated at Chislehurst, where one of his fellow pupils was the young Malcolm Campbell. The pair soon discovered a mutual fascination with wheeled vehicles, which resulted in a spectacular pile-up with a borrowed penny-farthing bicycle.

Soon, Davis was enthusiastically involved with motor vehicles and, after training as an illustrator, he joined Daimler as an apprentice, helping to build a wide variety of machines from Renard Road Trains to racing cars for the 1907 Kaiser-preis. His artistic talents were called into play to produce a series of 'rude little pictures' showing a sleeve-valve man triumphing over a poppet-valve man, with the aim of knocking Daimler's chief carriage-trade rival, Napier.

In 1910, he took up a new job, 'technical illustrator and general dogsbody', on the magazine *Automobile Engineer*, which was being launched by Iliffe, publishers of *The Autocar*; soon he was writing about cars as well as drawing them, and laying the foundations of his motor-racing career by competing in trials with light cars.

Motoring played a large part in his World War I career, too, for he was with a Royal Navy armoured division. One of their spare-time activities consisted of climbing and descending a hill, first on a 3½ hp Douglas motor cycle, then in a Talbot truck, next on a Rolls-Royce armoured car and finally in a four-wheel-drive Jeffery Quad truck, the winner being the one who completed the course quickest without mishap.

After the war, Davis became Sports Editor of *The Autocar*, in which capacity he helped his pre-war motor-cycling friend, W. O. Bentley launch his new sports car.

S. F. Edge invited Davis (who managed to combine his sporting activities with the deadlines of his job) to join his Brooklands AC team in 1921, then, in 1922, he helped Aston Martin smash 32 world and class records at the Weybridge track. Around the same time, he began entering trials with an ABC flat-twin light car, which at first had a fantastic ability to seize solid on hills; Waverley, Aston Martin and Frazer Nash were among other marques which he drove in contemporary road events.

In 1925, he drove a 3-litre, twin-cam Sunbeam at Le Mans with Jean Chassagne, and came within an ace of winning. The following year he was back, at the wheel of a 3-litre Bentley, which he contrived to crash 20 minutes from the end of the race while attempting to take the lead.

He crashed again at Le Mans in 1927, but this time it was an accident that became part of motoring mythology. Davis was driving the 3-litre Bentley known as 'Old Number Seven' into White House Corner when he noticed that the roadside fence had been damaged during his last lap, so he immediately slowed down. Just around the corner was a tangle of crashed cars, into which Davis managed to skid sideways to

Sammy Davis, in the 1930 Brooklands 500 Mile-winning Austin Seven

minimise damage. Even so, when he extricated the Bentley from the wreckage, he found it had a twisted chassis in addition to more superficial damage, yet managed to persuade the car to stay together long enough to win.

Davis was not just a Bentley Boy though for, in 1927, he won the Essex Six Hours' Race at Brooklands with a 12/50 Alvis, a marque to which he transferred his allegiance for the 1928 Le Mans, coming in ninth at the wheel of a 1500 cc, front-wheel-drive car, partnered by Urquhart-Dykes. Sammy also drove a Riley in that year's Tourist Trophy, while in 1929 he was in the Lea-Francis team, with a 1500 cc Hyper. He came second in the Saorstat Cup at Phoenix Park, Dublin and was also second in the Brooklands Double-Twelve and 500-mile races.

In between times, he acquired an 1897 Bollée tri-car in France, his enthusiasm for such antique vehicles leading him to become one of the three founders of the Veteran Car Club in 1930. Davis, who wrote under the pseudonym 'Casque', and his assistant, L. V. Head ('Caput'), campaigned the Bollée—christened Beelzebub—in pre-war Brighton Runs; indeed, Davis continued to drive Beelzebub in the Brighton until the late 1960s, when he was entering his 80s, his doctor then warning him that this sort of activity was hardly suitable for an octogenarian. The Bollée was sold to the Indianapolis Speedway Museum.

The year 1930 was a vintage, as well as a veteran, one for Davis, for the little Austin Seven he co-drove with the Earl of March won

the Brooklands 500-miles race at the astonishing average of 83.41 mph, then added to its fame by carrying off several Class H records, including a flying kilometre at 89.08 mph. On that occasion, Davis's co-driver was Charles Goodacre. Sammy's successes during the season were so numerous that he was awarded a BRDC Gold Star. Off the track, he drove a Double-Six Daimler in the Monte Carlo Rally, an event in which he subsequently entered a Railton tourer, an Armstrong Siddeley and a Sunbeam-Talbot; the Wolseley he drove in this event in 1937, won a special award for being the best equipped vehicle to finish.

Davis's racing career came to an abrupt hiatus at Brooklands in 1931, when the low-chassis Invicta he was driving skidded into a telegraph pole. During his spell in hospital, he wrote the classic book *Motor Racing*.

In 1935, he was driving a Singer Nine in the TT when a ball-joint in the steering fractured, and the car left the road, rolling over on Norman Black's sister car, which had crashed at the same spot for the same reason. Despite the serious nature of the crash, Davis escaped this time without injury, apart from a scratch where his helmet had been knocked off.

Long after his retirement from active competition, Davis—with his habitual beret and pipe—was a familiar figure at motor-sporting venues and, when well into his 80s, the seemingly indestructible Sammy was still writing, drawing and painting with unabated vigour.   DBW

SOMETHING SPECIAL FOR THE ENTHUSIAST

Above: Adrian Evans stands beside his creation: the Davrian Imp sports. Though the little car may be thought odd-looking by some people, and even ugly by others, it is loved by the people who buy it because of its sheer 'roadability' which, they claim, is what one buys a sports car for

AS AUTOMOTIVE ENGINEERS, the English have always been more influenced by social background and economic circumstance than those of virtually any other country. A close scrutiny of those 'lost causes' of the UK motor industry, which have either vanished or become the scrap dealer's stock in trade, can always be correlated to economic forces which have moulded, if not forced, many of the more adventurous people into financial cul-de-sacs from which they could not escape.

However, the consolidation of the UK motor industry has now led to a situation which has created a more secure climate for the truly original entrepreneur to operate in. The disappearance of many companies through merger, acquisition, of inertia of financial incompetence has brought about a situation in which anyone seeking to bring something fresh to the market place, must take advantage of the major research carried out by other, richer concerns. Through engineering circumstance, the major companies now produce a catalogue of equipment which, when judiciously blended, can be made into a convincingly homogeneous creation which owes everything to somebody but, perhaps more important, something to everyone.

Historically speaking, the mid 1960s could well have been the apogee of the type of small company which took 'off-the-shelf' items from standard cars and arrived at a vehicle specification which proved to be simple to construct yet which endowed the finished motor car with reserves of power, roadholding and handling far in excess of the rather prosaic motor cars produced by the big companies.

A typical example of this kind of approach is in the products of Davrian Developments, a small, London-based company, which specialises in producing a light, extremely quick two-seat coupé which uses, as its basis, the mechanical components of the Chrysler Imp of 875 or 998 cc.

First introduced in 1965, the Davrian is the product of the fertile and well-tutored mind of Adrian Evans who, by profession, is a structural engineer but by nature an entrepreneural motoring enthusiast. However, to leave a statement like that standing on its own would be to ignore the fact that the Imp was midwifed into the automotive world by Mike Parkes, a man with an impeccable motor-industry pedigree who at one time worked for Ferrari as a development engineer and who was also talented enough to drive cars in both Formula One and international sports-car races.

Given, therefore, the fact that Imp components were designed and produced to the highest standards possible for a small, light car aimed at the mass motoring market, it follows that the proper utilisation of those components into a smaller, lighter motor car which had to make no concessions to the dictates of mass-market parameters would mean that the finished product should be exceptionally quick yet economical.

Such has proved to be the case. Viewed financially, the continuing success of the Davrian proves to be almost amazing, especially if one looks back in retrospect and considers the number of talented concerns which have been forced out of business since those halcyon days of the early to mid 1960s. Considered mechanically, though, it is no wonder that this simple, yet extremely successful, car, should continue to be popular with sufficient enthusiasts to ensure the continuing health of Davrian Developments.

Based on the Imp, then, the Davrian story is one of constant development in the hands of a talented and trained engineer allied to easy access to a sub-industry only too willing to provide special equipment for tuning both the Imp engine and the car's original suspension.

The car is basically an adapted monocoque centre section—complete with a contoured interior—on which the mechanical components are hung. Three major glassfibre mouldings are produced, these providing the undertray or platform complete with wheel arches, the interior pan and the one-piece outer section. Smaller mouldings and the extensive use of polyurethane foam, injected into the body's cavities, ensure that the basic car is rigid, strong, easy to repair but, above all, light. A bonded-in engine support enables the structure to carry the heaviest mechanical components in a neat yet practical manner.

Standard Imp running gear is simply hung on the very strong, light structure to produce a vehicle which turns the scales at 4 cwt under the all-up weight of the normal production Imp. It can be seen and appreciated, therefore, that the Davrian should be considerably quicker than the standard Imp, and the road performance and competitive success of the Davrian would appear to bear this out. These basic factors allied to an extremely good aerodynamic shape and the minimum of extraneous equipment combine to make the Davrian one of the neatest, lightest cars available to the enthusiast. Some Davrians are made to take rear-mounted Volkswagen engines or mid-mounted Mini units but still use the same body type.

With its roots basically in the early kit-car days, yet its future even more firmly in the market of supplying that special yet not exorbitantly expensive motor car for the enthusiast, it would appear that, in 1974, Davrian Developments has more of a future than it does a past. TN

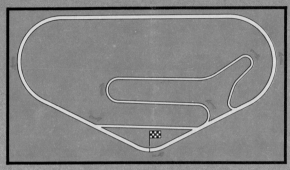

Daytona

TO AN OLDER MOTOR SPORTING FAN, the name Daytona conjures up visions of speed record attempts on the hard-packed sands of Daytona Beach. That changed in 1958 when bulldozers rumbled in on the swampland nearby and created the Daytona International Speedway, which was, until recently, the world's fastest oval race track. The man behind the project was super-promoter Bill France, the man who also created the National Association for Stock Car Auto Racing—NASCAR—which promotes racing for spectator-thrilling, 200 mph stock (the American term for 'standard') saloon cars on oval race tracks. NASCAR, Bill France and Daytona are synonymous.

Daytona Beach, in north-east Florida, is a 23-mile stretch of sand (500 yards wide at low tide) which was first used for automobile speed trials in 1903. The actual town of Daytona Beach, with a population of over 45,000, is situated either side of the Indian River and its history dates back to a community which settled in the area over 100 years ago.

The world land-speed record was attacked many times at Daytona Beach. In 1904, William K. Vanderbilt established an unofficial land-speed record at 92.307 mph. His car was a Mercedes 90. By 1905, Herbert L. Bowden, at the wheel of a 120 bhp Mercedes, had achieved 109.75 mph. In 1910, Barney Oldfield's Blitzen Benz motored over the measured mile at an average of 132.04 mph. Between 1927 and 1935, the record was continually being passed between

Below: a pit-front scene at Daytona Speedway, home of the giant NASCAR 'stockers' and the Daytona sports-car series

Henry Segrave and Malcolm Campbell, the two daring British drivers finding that British venues were too small to contain their powerful steeds. Segrave set the ball rolling with the twin aero-engined Sunbeam '1000 hp' in March 1927, with an unofficial one-way record of 207.02 mph and an official two-way record of 203.79 mph. The 200 mph barrier had been broken.

In 1928, Malcolm Campbell ventured to Daytona Beach with one of his famous Bluebird record-breaking cars. It was powered by a specially-adapted Napier Lion aero engine and, despite fearsome skids, raised the record to 206.96 mph for the official two-way runs. Then the Americans tried to wrest the honour from Britain. Frank Lockhart's incredible 16-cylinder, 400 bhp, 3-litre Stutz, known as the Black Hawk, did a one-way run of 203.45 mph in atrocious conditions; later a rear tyre failed, it overturned and flung out its driver, who was killed instantly. Fatal accidents were commonplace in the 'pioneer' days. American Lee Bible's car went out of control in 1929, somersaulted and killed a film cameraman as well as the driver. Earlier, Bible's car, the 81-litre White-Triplex (it used three Liberty aero engines which combined to give 1200 bhp), had raised the record to 207.55 mph in the hands of Ray Keech. Keech had an exciting second run: the giant car had jumped 50 ft after a bump, and an engine backfire burned his arm.

In March 1929, Segrave returned with the Sunbeam Golden Arrow, a machine powered by a Schneider

France entered the arena. William Henry Getty France, born in Washington DC on 26 September 1909, is a big man. He stands 6 ft 5 in and is built like a grizzly bear; his hobby is racing cars. In 1934, he was taking his wife, Annie, and his baby son, Bill Jr, to Miami when his car broke down at Daytona Beach.

Bill France never ventured further than Daytona Beach. He took various jobs—he became a petrol attendant and a painter and decorator—and raced his Ford Model T dirt-track car. Soon he found more satisfaction, and profit, from promoting the races. Races around barrels on the beach became a popular entertainment and sometimes Bill and an associate would go inland into the country to promote races. Some of the competitors were 'moonshine men' taking time off from running illegal whiskey.

Racing stopped at the outbreak of World War II and Bill helped build warships at Daytona. Afterwards, in 1945, France promoted a race at Raleigh, North Carolina, but it was a flop. The following year, beach racing was revived at Daytona and it was an enormous success. Soon France extended his promotions to North and South Carolina and Georgia, and he pressed the American Automobile Association Contest Board, asking them to recognise officially his type of racing. He went to Washington and requested that a stock car division be formed for himself and other southern-based promoters.

France was scoffed at—but not defeated. In the

Trophy-type Napier Lion racing engine. With seeming ease, he stormed over the soaking wet sands to a new official record of 231.44 mph. Plans to try to boost this figure were cancelled after Lee Bible's accident. Until he found the 23-mile sands too dangerous for higher speeds and moved on to the Bonneville Salt Flats, Malcolm Campbell broke the record time and time again, leaving it at 276.816 mph on 7 March 1935. Campbell's last run—the final one ever at the venue for the ultimate record—was fraught with danger. Approaching the start of the measured mile with the throttles of the 2450 bhp Rolls-Royce R engine of 37 litres capacity wide open, Bluebird struck a bump in the sand. The five-ton monster left the ground, 'flew' for over 30 ft, crashed to the ground and tore the treads from the tyres. Campbell corrected a skid and went into the measured mile swaying from side to side with fragments of rubber flying from the wheels; yet he broke the record.

Into the 1930s, Daytona Beach was the scene of class record breaking and sand racing. This is when Bill

winter of 1947, 'Big Bill' arranged a meeting of interested parties at the Streamline Hotel, Daytona Beach. The National Association for Stock Car Auto Racing was born and France was its president.

NASCAR made stock-car racing respectable. France recalled: 'Looking back, before NASCAR, nobody had any interest in what happened to the contestant who got hurt. We were instrumental in developing a personal accident policy for race drivers and as far as I know, not one driver has failed to receive the money he raced for. Before NASCAR, it was not uncommon for a track operator to run off with the purse.'

Until his retirement in January 1972, Bill France remained strong at the helm. Almost single-handed he quashed threatened driver rebellions, he survived setbacks such as the American manufacturers' withdrawal from motor sport in the mid-1950s, and he remained respected. He remains as a consultant and as chairman of the board and president of the International Speedway Corporation. The ISC owns and operates two major speedway facilities, the one at

Below: some idea of the ultra-high-speed banked corners used at Daytona can be gained from this shot taken during the annual international sports-car race

Below left: a Chevrolet Corvette in action at Daytona

Daytona being the result of France's post-war dream.

From 1950, special circuits—oval speedways—were built for NASCAR racing. The first was the small, 1.25-mile, Darlington track (subsequently enlarged to 1.33 miles in 1953), but France's dream concerned Daytona Beach itself. He longed for a 'super speedway' free of the whims of the tide and weather conditions. In 1959, Daytona International Speedway was opened on reclaimed swampland; all action was now 12 miles from the town of Daytona Beach; the sands returned to the sun-worshippers full-time.

The construction of Daytona International Speedway, a 2.5-mile 'tri-oval' was a remarkable achievement. In order that the 31-degree banked sections be built, hundreds of thousands of tons of earth had to be moved from the centre of the infield. Into the resultant hole, gallons of water were pumped and a new inland waterway, Lake Lloyd, was formed and filled with 65,000 fish. Never one to miss an opportunity, France arranged speed-boat racing on the lake.

The circuit's facilities were second to none upon completion in 1959. Even today, few circuits can rival it. At least 90% of the circuit can be seen from any vantage point, including the infield 'road-type' loop which makes the circuit suitable for conventional racing cars as well as the oval-track cars.

Equally as remarkable was the result of the first major race, the first-ever Daytona 500 for NASCAR stock cars. Lee Petty beat Johnny Beauchamp, but it took three days for officials to determine Petty as the winner from a photo-finish. In April, Indianapolis-type machinery (USAC Formula cars) battled it out on the Speedway. Dick Rathman and Rodger Ward battled for the lead, but both were overtaken by Jim Rathman whose time for the 100-mile race was 35 m 24 s. This represents an average speed of 170.26 mph and, at the time, it was the fastest motor race ever run. Sadly, as he tried to snatch third place in a last-ditch attempt, George Amick lost control on the banking; his car struck the retaining wall and he was killed instantly. On the following day, a 1000-km sports car race was planned, using the infield section, but it had to be shortened to 560 miles owing to darkness. Winners were Argentine's Roberto Mieres and Brazil's Fritz d'Orey whose 1½-litre Porsche RSK humbled many more powerful cars which proved too fragile.

Stock car races are what makes Daytona pay. Every February, the 500-mile race is the highlight of the NASCAR calendar with 200,000 people attending a month of speed. First of all, a long-distance sports car race is run on the 3.81-mile combined track/infield circuit, then qualifying races for the 'stockers' at speeds of around 185 mph—this is the average for the 2.5-mile track (in qualifying for the 1974 Daytona 500, Dave Pearson lapped his 1973-model Mercury in 48.644 s, an average speed of 185.017 mph). Then follow the 125-mile preliminary races and finally the long-awaited Daytona 500.

To European eyes, the sports car race is the most interesting. Known as the 'Daytona Continental', it started as a three-hour race in 1962, grew to 2000-km in 1964 and became a 24-hour race to rival the French Le Mans 24-hours in 1966. In 1972, it temporarily reverted to a six-hour race, while the 1974 race was cancelled altogether owing to the energy crisis.

In 1974, France's son, Bill Jr, was President of NASCAR. Then 41, he grew up at Daytona. As well as having competed in races, he had vast experience of officiating in many capacities. Brother Jim France was Vice-President and Secretary of NASCAR while Big Bill's wife Annie was still Treasurer; a position she had held since NASCAR's inception in 1948. **MK**

CLEANING THE COMBUSTION SPACES

When the useful part of hydrocarbon fuel is burnt away, carbon deposits are left. Removing these leads to greater engine efficiency which means better performance and fuel consumption, and longer engine life

Left: a rotary wire brush, fitted to an electric drill, is very useful for removing deposits from the valve throats. The valve guides will probably prevent deep penetration, but a very small area will be left untouched if the brush is inserted through the ports, as well as through the throats

Above right: the most stubborn deposits may have to be removed from the valves with a scraper, but it is possible to take off most of the carbon by inserting each valve in the chuck of an electric drill.

Centre right: valve-grinding paste should be smeared round the seating surface of each valve prior to grinding in. If pitting is evident, coarse paste should be used before finishing off with fine

Below right: a special valve-grinding tool, with a rubber suction cup, should be used if the valves do not possess screwdriver grooves. Twisting the tool to and fro between the hands will remove any valve-seat imperfections

ANY ENGINE WHICH RUNS on a hydrocarbon fuel is likely to suffer from a build-up of carbon deposits. Whether that engine be conventional petrol or diesel, rotary or even gas turbine, the same principle applies, but for the time being we will confine ourselves to discussing reciprocating petrol engines.

There are three main reasons why carbon deposits are unwanted: gas flow is slowed down, combustion chamber size is decreased and 'hot spots' may be formed.

The basic governing factor for the efficiency of this type of engine is the rate at which the fuel/air mixture can enter each cylinder and the rate at which exhaust gases can leave. Smooth-sided passages are better than rough-sided ones, since the latter cause excessive turbulence and restrict the gas flow. Carbon deposits are, by nature, rough and therefore impair this efficiency.

A moderately tuned engine may not suffer by having its compression ratio raised, which is what happens as the combustion chamber size decreases, but others may begin to 'pink' (a tinkling noise caused by pre-ignition).

Pre-ignition is not always due to an over-high compression ratio, it may be caused by a 'hot spot'. The heat-conducting properties of carbon are not nearly so good as those of cast iron or aluminium alloy, so heat built up by combustion can be stored in the layer of carbon, eventually reaching red heat and causing fuel to ignite while the piston is still approaching the top of its stroke.

One of the most common symptoms of excessive carbonisation is 'running on' (the engine continues to run for some seconds after the ignition has been switched off). If either this phenomenon or 'pinking'

are present in a petrol engine, and the recommended grade of fuel is being used, excessive carbon build up must be suspected.

The only really effective way of decarbonising an engine is to take off the cylinder head and scrape the various parts free of this element. There are 'decarbonising agents' on the market which can be introduced to the combustion spaces via the spark-plug holes. Leaving these solvents in for several hours is supposed to free the engine of its deposits but, unfortunately, it is very difficult to remove anything other than a thin surface coating in this manner.

In any engine other than an overhead-camshaft power unit, removal of the cylinder head is a straight-forward job requiring only the disconnection of ancillaries, such as the exhaust pipe, coolant pipes, fuel pipe(s), wires and control cables and the disengagement of several fixing bolts or nuts. The carburettor(s) can often be left undisturbed, although, if the decarbonisation process is to be carried out properly, it or they should be removed at some stage to give access to the induction ports.

Of course, should the engine have side valves, it is quite possible that nothing other than the cylinder-head fixings need be undone—the inlet and exhaust will remain on the engine. However, it may still be desirable to take off at least the induction manifold, to avoid foreign bodies entering it and thence the carburettor(s).

Overhead camshafts present a slightly greater problem, in that the drive to the shafts, and sometimes the shafts themselves, have to be removed. In fact, refitting of the shafts involves far more work than does removal, since the valve timing has to be adjusted. Great care should be taken when refitting a camshaft, to make

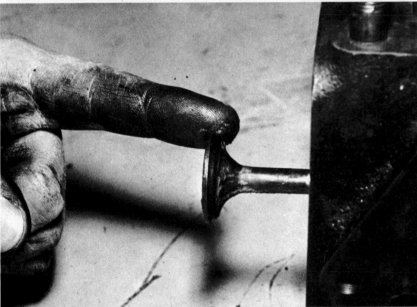

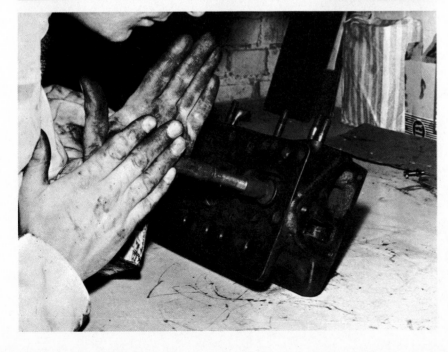

sure that none of the valves hit a piston; the safest avoiding action is to set the crankshaft so that all the pistons are below the top of their strokes.

If the job is to be carried out properly, the valves must all be removed and kept so that they can be replaced in their original seats. Probably the easiest way of remembering the order is to place all the valve stems, in order, through holes in a piece of card, numbering each hole accordingly.

A side-valve engine usually has a plate bolted to the side of the cylinder block, to give access to the valve fixings and valve springs. If the valves are to be removed from an overhead-camshaft engine, the shaft or shafts will have to be removed before the valve-spring compressor is brought into play. With overhead valves and a block-mounted camshaft, the rocker shaft will have to be unbolted in order to clear the way for valve removal.

Once the valves are out and marked, the process of decarbonisation can be started. A rotary wire brush, fitted to an electric drill, is very useful for cleaning the combustion chambers—from which the spark plugs should have been removed—but stubborn particles should be scraped off, using wood if possible, but soft metal if necessary.

The rotary brush can be used to clean out the valve throats and the ports (assuming the manifolds have been removed). The valves themselves can be cleaned by placing them in the chuck of the electric drill and using a scraper to clean the carbon from the head. Care should be exercised here, as it is essential to avoid damaging the valve seat and the stem where it passes through the guide in the cylinder head. Once the major part of the deposit has been removed, the valve can be polished with wet-or-dry paper.

Polishing is not essential for any of the parts, but it will take longer for carbon to build-up on a smooth, shiny surface, with few imperfections, than on a dull surface with many pits and bumps. Unfortunately, this build-up cannot be avoided, but its delay can only increase efficiency, for the reasons mentioned earlier.

The valves should be ground to fit their seats, by resting them in place, with a little grinding paste between the contact surfaces, and twisting them to and fro with either a special suction tool or, in the case of grooved valve heads, a screwdriver. When the seats are an even matt grey, with no pits, the grinding paste should be removed, the stem oiled and the springs and fixing devices replaced. If oil seals are used on the valve stems, new ones should be obtained in order to keep oil consumption to a minimum.

The carbon should be scraped from each piston crown, once again with wood if possible. It is advisable to leave a small ring of carbon around the edge of each piston (about 3/16 in), so that any deposits in the space between the top piston rings and the crowns will not be disturbed and perhaps increase oil consumption.

As each piston is tackled, it should be placed at the top of its stroke and a piece of cloth used to cover the other cylinders and any oil passages. Loose carbon should be wiped away carefully.

Before replacing the cylinder head, its face and that of the block should be wiped and lightly greased to prevent the gasket sticking. A new gasket should always be used as the old one will have been flattened.

It is advisable to measure the tension of the nuts and bolts with a torque wrench, as uneven settings can lead to warping of the head and consequent leakage of compression, coolant or both.

Finally, valve clearances must be adjusted, as grinding the valve seats closes these up and too tight a setting may eventually lead to a burnt valve.   IW

ROAD-GOING ROLLING STOCK

Decauville not only built railway trains and rolling stock, they also made some interesting motor cars

Below: the 1898 Decauville *voiturelle,* like so many cars of the period, used a De Dion twin-cylinder engine of 489 cc. Note the hand-wheel on the offside of the car, ideally placed for starting the car from the driving seat

TURN-OF-THE-CENTURY French locomotive engineers must have been an insecure breed for, when the petrol car appeared on the scene, they rushed *en masse* to become motor manufacturers. Typical was the case of the Etablissements Decauville, renowned as manufacturers of narrow-gauge railway engines and rolling stock, with a factory at Petit-Bourg, near Corbeil, Seine-et-Oise who, in 1898, acquired manufacturing rights to the Guédon light car. As Léon Bollée had pre-empted the name *voiturette* for his three-wheeler, Decauville christened their car the *voiturelle*; it was a diminutive and spidery four-wheeler with a rear-mounted twin-cylinder engine composed of two De Dion tricycle cylinders mounted on a common crankcase. The power unit, of 489 cc, was claimed to develop 3 hp at 1200 rpm, and drove through a simple two-speed gear which was entirely devoid of lubrication.

An advanced feature of the car was the use of sliding-pillar independent front suspension in conjunction with pneumatic tyres; but the company nullified any advantages inherent in this layout by omitting to provide any suspension at all for the rear of the car. Indeed, it is quite likely that the independent front suspension was adopted for its cheapness of manufacture rather than for any consideration of comfort, though Decauville claimed that the *voiturelle* 'rolled very sweetly'.

By 1899, the *voiturelle* was being marketed in England by R. Moffat Ford, and being built under licence in Italy by Orio & Marchand, and in Germany by the Eisenach Company, under the name Wartburg.

Moffat Ford was quick to arrange demonstrations of the marque's abilities; at the Automobile Club's 1899 Richmond Show, there was a display of trick driving by a team of Decauvilles, whose drivers would pick up handkerchiefs from the ground while driving at full speed, or get out of the cars and leave them

running in circles on their own. 'They only seemed to need one winding up', commented Moffat Ford, who had apparently got his motive powers somewhat muddled, 'and they would go all day'.

The original *voiturelles* were air-cooled but, in 1900, a front-engined water-cooled 5 hp model was available, soon joined by an 8 hp-twin with a horse-shoe-shaped dashboard radiator and a bullet-nosed bonnet.

Already, the marque was making an appearance in competitions: their first success was the winning of the voiturette class in the 1898 Paris-Amsterdam race. Their crack driver, Leon Théry, later became known as 'the Chronometer' for the regularity with which he lapped, and he was to win the Gordon Bennett for France and Richard-Brasier in 1904–5; he first came to notice in the 1899 Tour de France Automobile, in which a team of Decauvilles were first, second and third in the voiturette class, led home by Gabriel (who would late win the Paris-Madrid race in a Mors) with Théry in second place.

The new models continued the run of success with victories in the voiturette classes of the Bordeaux-Biarritz and Paris-Rouen-Paris races in 1900. In the same year, a Decauville was awarded the *Daily Mail* prize in the English Thousand Miles Trial.

In 1901, a four-cylinder Decauville made its appearance; its 3-litre engine was basically two 8 hp units mounted end-to-end. By this time, the idiosyncratic suspension layout of the *voiturelle* had been abandoned in favour of more conventional springing all round, and the light cars were dropped in 1902.

A new 10 hp model with a twin-cylinder, side-valve engine appeared for the 1902 season; it was chiefly remarkable for its pioneering use of unit construction for the engine, clutch and gearbox. Henry Royce bought one of these cars and copied its design and general layout for his first two-cylinder Royce car, progenitor of the Rolls-Royce. However, his failure to see the advantages of the engine/gearbox unit rather gives the lie to the often reported story that it was the poor design of the Decauville which drove Royce into motor-manufacture.

By 1906, a five-model range was on the market, all four-cylinder cars ranging from the 12/16 (actually of 20.1 rated horse-power) through the 16/20, 24/28 and 30 hp models, which also bore a far higher taxable horse-power than the manufacturers' classifications showed, to the massive 45 hp chain-driven model which sold at £1020 complete.

That seems to have been the high point of the marque's career, for the following year the range was axed drastically, leaving only the 12/16 and 16/20.

H. M. Hobson, who had taken over the British agency from Moffat Ford's International Motor Car Company, continued to sell these two models alongside the Nagant-Hobson until 1909. They attracted coachwork from some of the more obscure body builders of the day, such as Laurie & Marner, but were obviously over-priced compared with Mr Hobson's other choices.

Even in their native France, the Decauvilles were going out of favour with the buying public; by 1911, the company had given up car-manufacture altogether.

Car building, in any case, had been rather an irrelevant diversion for a company whose past achievements had included a railway engine which had been dismantled into two parts for an elephant to carry it across the mountains of the Bolan Pass in Turkestan, so that the British army could use it against the Russians in 1885. The enemy, it should be noted, were operating a similar Decauville railway!   DBW

FRANCE'S VETERAN CAR MANUFACTURER

Founded in 1684, the De Dietrich
company built its first car in the 1890s

THEY CALLED IT THE Société Lorraine des Anciens
Etablissements de Dietrich & Cie: and the *Etablissements* really were *anciens*, for the company had been
founded as long ago as 1684 by Jean de Dietrich. By the
time it became interested in motor-manufacture in the
1890s, the company was mainly concerned with the
production of railway rolling stock. It was still under
family control, though the Franco-Prussian war of
1870 had left their two manufacturing plants, at
Lunéville (Lorraine) and Niederbronn (Alsace), in two
different countries. In charge of the Lunéville operation was the Baron Adrien de Turckheim, who acquired
manufacturing rights to a design by Amédée Bollée jnr
in 1896.

These Bollée-Dietrich cars were chiefly remarkable
for their transmission: a horizontal-
twin engine drove, by belt, a sliding
gear box, with clutch action achieved by
loosening the belts; from the transverse
countershaft incorporating the differential,
propeller shafts took the drive to each rear wheel.
Spiral bevel gears were used at either end of the
propeller shafts; it was the first time this form of
gearing had been employed in a car.

At first, Bollée built the engines, while De Dietrich

Above: two 1899 6 hps

Below: a beautifully
restored 1903 tourer

made the rest of the vehicle. Soon, however, the entire car was being produced at Lunéville. The next major development was the construction of the four-cylinder, independent-front-suspension Bollée *Torpilleur* racing cars. These made a notable showing in the 1898 Paris-Amsterdam trials, in which Gaudry's car finished third, despite a crash *en route*. The performance of the cars aroused such enthusiasm that, during the weeks following the Paris-Amsterdam event, De Dietrich received orders totalling more than a million gold francs. One customer, the Comte de Paiva, commissioned what must have been one of the world's first streamlined sports cars; its coachwork by Rheims & Auscher incorporated a raked windscreen.

However, the next joint venture of Bollée and De Dietrich, the advanced *torpilleur* of 1899, with underslung chassis, rear-mounted four-cylinder, mono-block engine and twin carburettors, was less successful, due to insufficient preparation, and none of the works team completed the Tour de France race for which it had been designed. Despite pressure from Turckheim, Bollée decided to withdraw from competition and, though the Bollée-Dietrichs survived into the new century, latterly with chain drive, they were soon replaced in production by a neat little voiturette built under licence from Vivinus of Belgium in the Niederbronn factory, and by the Marseilles-designed Turcat-Méry at Lunéville.

Looking around for a car to replace the voiturette from Niederbronn, Eugène de Dietrich saw a neat four-cylinder, four-speed car which had been designed by the 19-year-old Ettore Bugatti, financed by the Count Gulinelli; the vehicle had won an award from the Automobile Club of France in 1899, and a gold medal at the Milan Exhibition of 1901. By 1902, Bugatti was on the pay roll at Niederbronn and had designed a 24 hp, four-speed, four-cylinder model with overhead-valves operated by pull-rods.

Bugatti produced a second model towards the end of 1903, a 30/35 hp De Dietrich; both the 24/28 and the 30/35 were marketed in Britain by the Burlington Carriage Co, who also handled the products of Lunéville. However, the Niederbronn cars were sometimes sold as Burlingtons, while the Lunéville cars always retained the De Dietrich label (sometimes suffixed by Turcat-Méry). Though Bugatti left De Dietrich in 1904 to join Mathis at Strasbourg, where he designed the Hermès car, Burlington kept up their association with him, selling the 40 hp Bugatti-Hermès alongside the De Dietrichs in 1905. This was the result of Niederbronn's decision to leave car production to Lunéville; from the end of 1904, the Alsatian market was supplied with Turcat-Mérys (the genuine Marseillaise item) imported by Mathis and fitted with De Dietrich badges.

To emphasise their independence from this arrangement, Lunéville soon renamed their cars Lorraine-Dietrich; they carried the cross of Lorraine on their radiator as an indication of their French nationality.

Behind their impressive new radiator, the Lunéville cars were still Turcat-Mérys—and remained so until 1911—though they had little in common with the range of four models (8 hp-twin and 12, 16 and 24 hp-fours) which had begun the association in 1902. The Lorraine-Dietrichs were handsome machines, with a reputation as one of the top half-dozen quality marques, ranking with cars such as Itala and Crossley. Around 1905–8, they even built a handful of super-luxury six-wheeled cars, at costs up to £4000 for a *limousine de voyage*.

In part, the marque's reputation was built on its competition record, which was consistent if not distinguished: highlights included third place for Charles Jarrott in the 1903 Paris-Madrid, and a 1-2-3 victory in the 1906 Circuit des Ardennes for the star works driver Léon Duray.

Apart from the smallest model, the 14 hp, all the 1908 De Dietrich touring cars were chain-driven, the range consisting of four fours—18/28 hp, 28/38 hp, 40/45 hp and 60/80 hp—priced between £550-£960, and a monstrous 70/80 hp six at a chassis price of £1040.

By now, the company was flexing expansionist muscles and, in 1907, had signed an agreement with Isotta-Fraschini in which they acquired control of the Milanese company; the cars built during this period of association, which ended in 1911, included two overhead-camshaft cars, the smaller of which was the 1.4-litre, 10 hp model apochryphally credited to Ettore Bugatti.

In 1907, the Lorraine-Dietrich company bought the factory of Ariel Motors Limited of Birmingham to produce a British Lorraine-Dietrich. One model only was made: a four-cylinder, 20 hp car which made its debut at the 1908 Olympia Motor Show, where three items—a polished chassis, a Mulliner cabriolet and a convertible by Salmons—were exhibited. The British cars differed from their French counterparts only by having shaft instead of chain drive and were marketed through the same sales organisation, Charles Jarrott & Letts of London. It was a venture which lasted only a year or so, and resulted in a loss for the parent company.

The Lorraine-Dietrich line-up in the immediate

pre-war period consisted of three quality touring cars, a 12/16, an 18/20 and a new 20/30, plus a 40/75 four-cylinder, semi-racing model; the entire range was now shaft-driven.

By now, production was concentrated at the company's new factory at Argenteuil, Seine-et-Oise, which became the company's headquarters after World War I.

In 1919, the company's new technical director, Marius Barbarou, produced the first post-war model, the 15 hp. As Barbarou had come to Lorraine-Dietrich from Delaunay-Belleville, the new car was naturally a six-cylinder, and was originally made in two wheelbase types, the A1-6 and the B2-6. In 1922, a further development, the B3-6, appeared with a choice of short or long-wheelbase chassis. The 15 hp had a swept volume of 3.4 litres, with overhead-valves in hemispherical heads, a four-bearing crankshaft and aluminium pistons.

Barbarou's original intention was to produce a moderately priced touring car of quality, but it soon became apparent that the performance of this model was worthy of a sporting variant. This fact was under-

lined in 1923, when a team of three touring Lorraines put up a passable showing in the first Le Mans 24-hour race. For the 1924 event, Barbarou designed the 15 Sport, with twin carburettors, oversize valves and four-wheel braking with Dewandre-Reprusseau servo assistance; the cars took second and third places and established themselves as the French equivalent of the 3-litre Bentley.

In 1925, the 15 Sport of Courcelle and Rossignol took first place at Le Mans, with a sister car in third position. The next year was even better: Bloch and Rossignol came first at an average speed of 66 mph, a record speed for the event, with Lorraines in second and third positions.

In the reflected glory of these sporting achievements, the touring 15 hps—known in Britain as 'The Silken Six'—acquired a new glamour. The undistinguished coachwork of the earlier models was replaced by more stylish bodies, mostly from the firm of Gaston Grummer, who was also commercial director at Argenteuil; his products bore such names as Gloriosa, Aurora, Olympia, Gloria and Chiquita. Alongside the 15 hp were sold two other touring models, the four-cylinder 12 hp ('agréable et pratique') and the 30 hp six. The larger model lasted until 1927, while the smaller continued until 1929.

As for the 'élégant et inimitable' 15 hp, it survived in production until 1932, when it was succeeded by a new 20 hp, four-litre model; the 15 Sport had been discontinued in 1930, and had just missed ending its distinguished career with one final victory when the 22-year-old Jean-Pierre Wimille had lost the 1931 Monte Carlo Rally by one-tenth of a decimal point to Donald Healey's Invicta.

Only a few hundred of the elegant 20 hp models were built, and sales were far from encouraging. The model's effective production life was only a couple of years, and by 1935 the name of Lorraine-Dietrich had vanished from the motor industry. Since 1930, the company had been part of the Société Générale Aéronautique, a consortium of aircraft manufacturers, and Argenteuil went over to the manufacture of aero engines and military six-wheelers built under licence from the Czech firm of Tatra.

And Lunéville? Once it had ceased to be a centre of car production, it reverted to its former ways, and was still in business in 1974 as a manufacturer of railway ironmongery.   DBW

Left top: a 1902 De Dietrich, based on a Turcat Méry design. Turcat Méry, who were short of capital, signed an agreement with De Dietrich to design cars for them in 1901

Left centre: de Dietrich at the wheel of one of his 1903 racers

Left bottom: Lunéville renamed its cars Lorraine-Dietrich as a mark of independence. Note the cross of Lorraine on the radiator of this 1912, 15-litre example.

Below: a 1903 chain-drive Spider

THE ARISTOCRAT AND THE TOYMAKER

It was an unlikely combination, the wealthy Parisian nobleman and the penniless model maker, yet together they took the motoring world by storm

IN THE SCINTILLATING CITY of Paris in the 1880s, few names were better known than that of Albert, Comte de Dion, scion of one of France's most distinguished noble families. He was, by all accounts, a fast liver—and a notorious duellist—with a passion for machinery which somewhat distressed his family. But, added a contemporary: 'He was more often seen in society drawing-rooms and even gaming-rooms, than in workshops and laboratories'.

It was, in fact, when he was strolling down the fashionable Boulevard des Italiens in Paris, late in 1881, in search of gifts for the ladies at a New Year's ball he was helping to organise, that De Dion made the discovery that was to lead to his becoming the keenest driving force and most powerful creator in the

Top: Albert, Comte de Dion

Far left: an 1889 De Dion steam wagon now housed in a military museum

Above left: in advertising their 1902 single-cylinder runabout, De Dion worked on the theme that their cars were such a joy to drive that their prospective buyers would probably sack the chauffeur so the owner could drive the car. The chauffeur in the poster can obviously see this happening

Below left: in the laboratory of their factory, Albert de Dion, *left*, and Georges Bouton, *right*

early history of motor industry and motor sport.

In the window of the novelty shop run by one Giroux was a tiny model steam engine fired by methylated spirits. De Dion knew enough about steam engines to have built one some years previously, but this model was obviously special, for he not only bought it, but questioned Giroux about its makers, with a view to building a similar model.

He was told that the engine was the work of Georges Bouton, who had a tiny workshop in the passage Léon, in the rue de la Chapelle, where he and his brother-in-law, Trépardoux, made mechanical toys for Giroux, and showcase models for the Ducretet precision engineering company. De Dion hurried round to the passage Léon to find that the two men were working virtually at starvation level, with only a few pennies coming in each week; it took little persuasion—and very little money—for them to go into business with De Dion, who proposed building steam cars.

MARSEILLE-NICE 1896

BREAK DE DION

Top: a tile illustration of an early De Dion on the walls of the Michelin building in London

Above: a 1902 model K single-cylinder car

Right: two De Dion engines of the single-cylinder type that powered so many light cars at the turn of the century

Obviously, to build cars, they needed a lot more space than the small premises in the passage Léon could offer; they found what they were looking for, a dilapidated house with a largish garden, in the rue Pergolese, on the corner of the avenue de Malakoff.

There Trépardoux, who was an accomplished steam-engineer, devised a boiler with an integral fire-box; this was installed in a spidery four-wheeled chassis, in which the engine drove the front wheels by twin belts, and the rear wheels steered. The car was running in 1883, and it was not long before a much-improved three-wheeled version, with conventional steering and rear-wheel drive, made its appearance. This formed the basis for a production steam tricycle, of which several examples were sold during the 1880s.

Already, however, the tall, portly De Dion and the short, heavily moustached Bouton were swinging away from steam as a motive force and experimenting with petrol engines of advanced design, including a ten-cylinder rotary in 1889.

Such activities were pure heresy to Trépardoux, who became more and more unhappy with the way the partnership was going. In 1894, this sullen defender of steam had had enough and resigned, though not before he had designed a steam break that featured an ingenious double rear axle, with the final drive mounted rigidly on the chassis, driving the rear wheels through universally jointed shafts. The weight of the car was carried on a dead tubular axle. Unfortunately for M. Trépardoux, this arrangement, still used on some modern cars to keep the unsprung weight down, has become immortalised as the de Dion rear axle and no longer bears any reference to him.

With Trépardoux gone, the design of the steamers changed little over their remaining decade of production; indeed, it is difficult to see why De Dion kept them going for so long, for this side of the venture brought no profit.

In any case, Bouton had, in 1895, produced a new power unit whose fame would eclipse anything that his brother-in-law had ever done: it was a tiny 137 cc petrol engine, which seemed a failure at first, for at its

Right: the chassis of the 1911 DM model showing its de Dion rear suspension. This was one of the last De Dion cars to feature such a system.

Below: the DM's V8 engine

designed engine speed of 900 rpm it ran irregularly and knocked out its bearings. However, when Bouton attempted to accelerate the engine further, he found that all the roughness disappeared completely, and reliability was vastly improved.

On the test-bench, he could run his first engine at the then fantastic speed of 3500 rpm, though in practice, 2000 rpm was a more realistic figure, taking account of the limitations of the rather primitive automatic inlet valve (sucked open by the piston on the induction stroke), the surface carburettor and the trembler-coil ignition. Bouton fitted this power unit in a tricycle, mounting it behind the rear axle, which it drove through roller gearing. The machine, which ran on the new-fangled pneumatic tyres, had an excellent performance; up-gradings of the engine (to $1\frac{1}{4}$ hp in 1896, then to $1\frac{3}{4}$ hp the next year) enhanced the De Dion's reputation for speed, and it became the accepted mount for young motorists with sporting inclinations.

L. Baudry de Saunier summed up the model's appeal in 1899: 'The De Dion Bouton tricycle, with its small, easily accessible components, fairly easily understood, even by a novice, and cheap to run, (for example, for the cost of five francs' worth of petrol, a tricycle and trailer could carry three people from Paris to Trouville) 'placed motoring within the reach of most people'.

The tricycle survived into 1901, by which time it was giving $2\frac{3}{4}$ hp; racing versions were built with engines up to 8 hp, which accentuated the model's tendency to rear-up under power.

A quadricycle had made a brief appearance in 1899, but was soon supplanted by the marque's first voitur-ette, the $3\frac{3}{4}$ hp rear engined model D, whose single-cylinder engine had a swept volume of 402 cc.

The production of such a machine was a logical step for De Dion, as the Count had been the prime mover in the formation of the Automobile Club of France in November 1895. The De Dion voiturette was an obvious progression from the tricycle for motorists who wanted more comfort and extra seating accommodation. At first, Bouton attempted to do away with rear suspension altogether but, before long, the design was altered to incorporate rear springing in conjunction with the axle layout originally conceived by Trépardoux for the 1894 steamer. Layout of the coachwork was unusual in that the driver occupied the rear seat, with the front seat passenger facing him. It was a concept which may have made for polite conversation but obviously cut down the driver's view of the road ahead.

The voiturette succeeded in spite of its curious coachwork and production facilities were expanded to meet the demand. In addition, De Dion Bouton had established themselves as engine manufacturers on a large scale, providing power units for other manu-facturers all over Europe. The engines were produced so rapidly that there was no time to check out any unit which failed to perform satisfactorily on the test bench. 'We just dismantle them and use them for spare parts,' explained Bouton. It was estimated that over 40,000 De Dion engines had been produced by 1904, at which time the company's work force at their new factory on the Quai National at Puteaux (Seine) had risen to 1300, with car production running at over 2000 annually.

Though the voiturette was hardly an inspiring per-former, it had the major advantage of an exceptionally easy two-speed gear-change by expanding clutches operated by a bar on the steering column. The rear-engined theme was progressively developed through models E, G, L, and J between 1899 and 1902, by which time horse-power had risen to six, and more conventional coachwork was available, including a rear entrance phaeton with a dummy bonnet. Then, in 1902, came the 8 hp model K, which combined a front-mounted engine with a coal-scuttle bonnet similar to that of the contemporary Renault.

An unusual feature of the control of these early De Dions (and one which persisted until World War I) was the decelerator pedal which progressively reduced engine speed, then applied the transmission brake. Reliability was an outstanding feature of this model, which accounted for its appeal to the medical pro-fession. Another key point was the smooth running of the single-cylinder engine, which developed its full

Above: a 1904, single-cylinder, 942 cc Type 2 De Dion Scooter. By 1904, a three-speed, expanding-clutch gearbox, first seen on the model O of 1902, had become standard throughout the range

Above left: a 1907 BG model, restored at the Biscaretti museum in Turin

Centre left: a 1912 sports DK and, *left below*, its four-cylinder engine, with exposed pushrods operating the side valves. By this time, De Dion had produced their V8, which was the last of the company's innovations

power at around 1600 rpm. Recalled one pioneer owner of a 1903 model Q, a low-priced variant of the K: 'The De Dion 6 was notably free from that everlasting dither which loosened the tooth stopping of so many early motorists.'

By 1903, the range had reached bewildering proportions: there were two 6 hp singles, the N and the Q, an 8, the R and the firm's first twin-cylinder model, the S, whose 12 hp engine was a doubling-up of the 6.

Three-speed transmission had made its first appearance on the model O of 1902, and, by 1904, was universal throughout the range. It was fashion rather than necessity which led to the replacement of the old expanding-clutch gear by a more conventional crash box on the 1905 models, which boasted four-cylinder variants, the model AD of 15 hp and the 24 hp AI. The last model to use the expanding gear was the 1906 AL 8 hp which also reverted to the tubular-steel

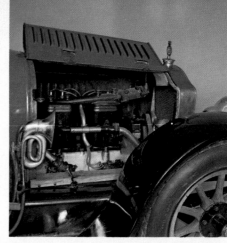

chassis of the earlier models, rather than the pressed-steel frames used from 1905 on. Despite an obvious demand for the old-type 8 hp, it was phased out by 1908. Typical of the dedicated owners of these vehicles was the County Surveyor of Devon, who wrote to the British agents in October 1907: 'The 6 hp De Dion I bought from you in September 1902 has travelled a distance equal to three times round the world (about 80,000 miles). The fibre in the expanding clutch has not been renewed. This, I consider, only proves to the highest degree the reliability of this type of gear.'

In 1907, the factory entered two 10 hp twins driven, without success, by Cormier and Collignon in the Peking to Paris race, while an adventurer named Bouvier St Chaffray competed with conspicuous lack of success in the 1908 New York-Paris event.

In many ways, the De Dion factory had passed its peak by 1908, and the subsequent models were in general conventional machines of no particular distinction at all.

However, Puteaux was to make one more contribution to motoring history—the world's first production V8 of any merit (Ader had pioneered this layout on his 1903 Paris-Madrid racers, while the 1906 Adams used the modified Antoinette aero engine). The De Dion V8 first appeared in 6.1-litre form in 1910, and was soon uprated to over 7 litres, then to 7.8 litres. There was even a gargantuan 14.7-litre variant, mainly aimed at the American market; at the opposite end of the size range was a 4-litre model introduced in 1912, but also being a V8.

During World War I, De Dion V8s fitted with 75 mm anti-aircraft guns were used to defend London against Zeppelins.

The V8 engine was, unfortunately, the last of the company's innovations; indeed, De Dion Bouton had dropped the distinctive de Dion axle in 1911, and their last single-cylinder model, the DE 1 of 1913, came off badly in comparison with its forebears.

After the war, the V8 continued in production to meet a gently declining demand until 1923. Alongside it were offered a range of light-fours of dated appearance, under the limp advertising slogan 'The car that holds the friendship of its owner'.

A more adventurous model, the 12/28 hp, was announced for 1923, with an overhead-valve engine and aluminium pistons. 'It is', eulogised its makers, 'a combination of lightness and strength, possesses rapid acceleration, a marked reserve of power on hills, is speedy and exceptionally well sprung.'

The 1923 models could be purchased with four-wheel braking at an extra cost of £30, which was said to result in 'an entire absence of skidding even on the worst of greasy roads'.

Rationalisation was hardly a feature of the 1923 models: the English concessionaires listed six variants of the side-valve 12/24 hp, a similar number of 12/28s, and six variations on the 15/43 hp V8, which had acquired overhead-valves for its last year of existence. Prices were reduced in an attempt to boost the flagging sales, but even the announcement of a new 1328 cc model, the side-valve JP type, could not avert the closure of the factory in 1927.

There were rumours that Peugot or Mercedes would take over at Puteaux, but somehow De Dion managed to get under way again, and even to announce a new model, a 2½-litre straight eight. Alongside this was offered the 2-litre 11 hp four, but few examples of either model reached the market. In 1930, the straight-eight had grown to 3 litres, but this move failed to avert the inevitable end of production. The last De

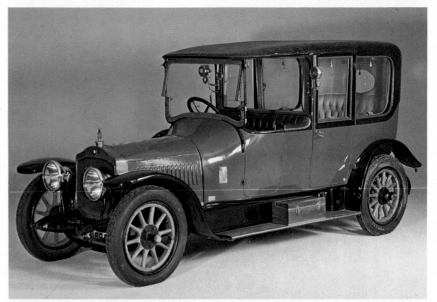

Dion car, an 11 hp, was delivered early in 1932, though commercials were listed until World War II.

Both the marque's founders survived the cars: Bouton died in 1938, while the Marquis De Dion (he had succeeded his father in 1901) lived through the war, occasionally taking the air in an ancient JP type driven by his decrepit coloured chauffeur, Zélélé; the pair celebrated the liberation of Paris by appearing on the streets in a 1900 vis-à-vis. The Marquis died the following year, 1946, at the age of 90.

There was a brief revival of the commercials after the war, but it was all over by the end of the 1940s, and the factory degenerated into a service garage.

Ironically, the De Dion Bouton name was acquired by a manufacturer of motor cycles in 1955: the wheel having come full circle, the once great marque just faded away.   DBW

Top and centre: a beautiful Type Ea of 1913. Note the tremendously high quality of the interior, especially the rosewood panelling on the inside of the door

Above: a 1914, four-cylinder Torpedo

THE FIRST STEP TO INDEPENDENCE

THE CLASSICAL LIVE REAR AXLE has two besetting sins which cannot be eradicated. One is that it is heavy: a large mass that is unsprung and therefore cannot be allowed the softness of springing and amplitude of travel that would be desirable for good ride and road-holding. The other is that it reacts to the tractive torque transmitted to it by the propeller shaft: it tries to turn about its own axis and about that of the pinion in the final drive gearing, producing spurious motions of the suspension and tending to lift one wheel (usually the right wheel) clear of the ground to the detriment of traction and handling. The sheer weight of the final drive aggravates this behaviour: it is the heaviest part of the assembly, and its mass concentrated midway between the extremities of the axle encourages the tramp and patter of the axle to proceed at high frequency, because of the low polar moment of inertia (force about a centre point) of the whole.

Independent rear suspension overcomes these problems but brings others in its train, notably the difficulty of minimising variations in wheel camber as the suspension flexes, while contriving to locate the instantaneous roll centre where the designer would like it to be. Many independent suspension systems create other problems, such as variations of toe-in, long-distance migration of the roll centre, the transmission of tyre vibrations, and the sheer amount of space necessary to accommodate their extensive link mechanisms.

All these difficulties may be set aside by employing the de Dion axle arrangements. Here, the final drive gears are set in a casing mounted firmly to the chassis, or other sprung part of the car's structure, communicating with the wheels by universally-jointed driving half-shafts just as in a conventional modern independent suspension system. The wheels, however, are mounted at the extremities of a rigid axle beam that may be located and sprung in much the same way as a live axle (the de Dion axle, since it plays no part in the transmission of engine torque, is 'dead') but without the same compromises having to be made. The suspension is relieved of tractive torque reactions; the wheels are kept at constant camber (usually zero, setting them perpendicular to a flat road) and never toe in or out; the total unsprung mass is moderate, comparable with that of an independent system; the designer is free to choose his suspension and location linkages so as to put the roll centre where he wants it; the axle assembly has a high polar moment of inertia and hence a low frequency of oscillation, which makes the selection of springs and dampers easier; and the whole arrangement need occupy scarcely more space than a conventional live axle.

The snags? They are very few. One is that the system costs more than a live axle; the other is shared with the live axle, in that the spring base (the distance between the springs on left and right of the car where they communicate with the axle) is narrower than the track or distance between the centrelines of the tyres, whereas in an independent suspension system the spring base is equal to the track. The importance of a wide spring base is that it allows the springs to be kept soft,

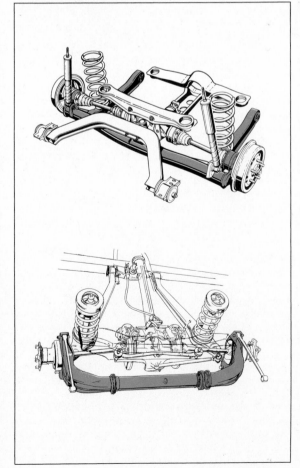

Above: an 1899 3½ hp De Dion chassis clearly shows the de Dion layout (the yellow curved beam behind the differential is the de Dion tube)

Left: two examples of the layout in modern use—*above*, as in the Rover 2000 and, *below*, as in the Opel Diplomat. The de Dion design employs most of the advantages of both independent and rigid systems with very few of the disadvantages

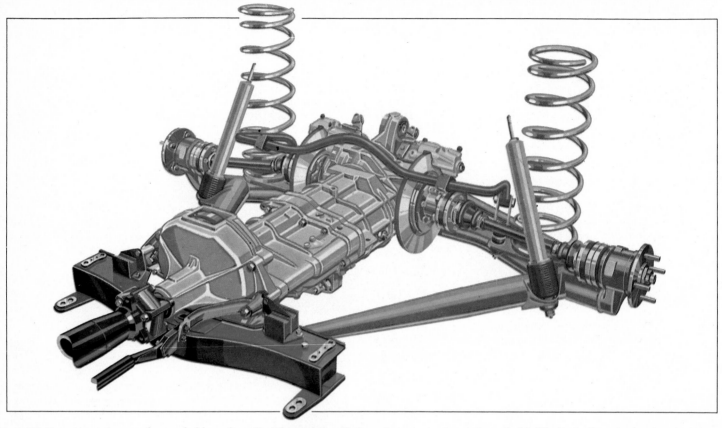

Alfa Romeo cars have been renowned for their excellent handling characteristics, although they have been fitted with rigid rear axles. In 1972, Alfa broke with tradition and introduced the Alfetta, named after the much-loved racer of 1947. The Alfetta featured a de Dion rear end linked with trailing arms and a transverse Watt linkage. This, combined with the car's gearbox which was integral with the rear suspension, gave the Alfetta remarkable handling and roadholding qualities

for good ride and roadholding, while offering adequate resistance to roll, as is desirable for good handling. The objection is not insuperable, for it is merely the conventions of suspension design that impose this penalty: Bristol designed (for an ill-fated prototype) a de Dion axle with spring base wider than the track, twenty years ago, and similar objects have been achieved in designs for commercial vehicles.

It is unlikely that the progenitor of the system envisaged any of its modern advantages, save the opportunity of mounting the final drive gearbox firmly on the chassis. De Dion and Bouton took out the patent in 1894; and from 1896 to 1910, the tubular dead axle and pot-jointed half-shafts were a feature of de Dion Bouton cars.

Thereafter the system was practically forgotten. The clever American engineer Miller used it for an Indianapolis car in 1924, and the system was adapted to his front-wheel-drive racers as well as the more old-fashioned kind, with such success that the layout was emulated in early models of the Cord, among other front-wheel-drive roadgoing cars. Horch in Germany adopted it for a touring car in the early 1930s, but it was in 1937 that the de Dion axle was put emphatically back on the map, when Daimler-Benz engineered a sophisticated version for their prodigiously powerful (and previously somewhat unmanageable) Mercedes-Benz Grand Prix cars. Thereafter, it became virtually mandatory for any first-class racing car. Not until 1959 was it overtaken by new developments in independent rear suspension, with Daimler-Benz again pioneers in their all-independent 1954 racers.

Since then, the de Dion axle has mainly featured in expensive high-performance cars built in modest numbers. The Lancia Aurelia (originally all-independent), the 4-litre Lagonda, the 4P Maserati and the Mark 2 Frazer-Nash were typical of the applications for which it was reserved; and not until the introduction of the DAF 66 in 1972 was it ever conceded that it had virtues of value to the small car of low power and moderate cost. In this form, with the axle beam

clamped to half-elliptic leaf springs, the de Dion suspension of the DAF reverted to the original type, shorn of such complexities as the oscillating joint that Daimler-Benz had to insert in their racer's axle beam to stop it functioning as an impossibly stiff anti-roll bar. It was merely the solecisms of the locating linkages that had made this device necessary in the Mercedes-Benz; and there were to be many others committed by racing-car designers in the ensuing years.

So far, the most refined version to appear has been in a production car of medium size, medium price, and medium performance: this is the Rover 2000 and its derivatives. In these, the axle tube has a sliding joint in it, not only permitting angular freedom to prevent it acting as an anti-roll bar but also allowing it to telescope slightly. This in turn permits the articulated drive shafts to be of fixed lengths, rendering splined or other slip joints otiose—and the tendency of such splines to bind when subjected to torque has always been a hindrance to the behaviour of all rivals to the live axle. In addition to these means of avoiding wear and tear and bad handling habits, the Rover system is further refined by the use of a Watt linkage (lower trailing and upper leading arms) to locate the hubs longitudinally and constrain them to move only in the vertical plane, eliminating roll-steer effects. Since the lateral location of the wheels is attended to by the drive shafts, lateral location of the axle beam is almost an irrelevance, and may safely be entrusted to the Panhard rod which in any other application must be considered a source of imperfect geometry.

From time to time, enthusiasts forecast a revival of the de Dion axle because it suits the characteristics of modern wide flat-crowned tyres which are rather sensitive to variations in camber. The latest tyre developments promise to make this argument untenable; but the system's other virtues will never cease to be worthy of cultivation, and the cyclical return to fashion of most automotive-engineering features may well be observed in the case of the de Dion axle in the future, as in the past. LJKS

SPEED AND ELEGANCE IN THE FRENCH TRADITION

In 1905, Louis Delage took the gamble of a lifetime to form his own motor company. Today, his cars are a legend of motoring

LOUIS DELAGE, founder of one of the greatest firms in the French automobile industry, was born in Cognac in 1874. At the age of fifteen he left school and started studying engineering. Despite having the sight of only one eye, since birth, he did well, and acquired a position in a public works engineering department. After a short time he joined the Turgan-Foy company as a draughtsman and, after a few years, he moved to Automobiles Peugeot. Both these firms were situated in Levallois, a western suburb of Paris.

Delage soon established himself as manager of the experimental and testing department at Peugeot, but he was very ambitious and wanted to be his own boss.

At considerable risk, he borrowed 35,000 francs from a few backers and in 1905 set up a business of his own to manufacture cars in a small workshop. He had two lathes and three workmen, and had given up a salary of 600 francs a month to work for only one third of that. He had, however, brought with him Peugeot's chief designer, Legros, and it was through collaboration with Legros that the fame and fortune of Automobiles Delage was founded. In the beginning, they made parts for the Helbé car, which was assembled at Boulogne-sur-Mer with a De Dion engine.

The first Delages appeared in 1906, and were *voiturettes* built on sound, conservative lines. There was only one chassis style, which could be powered by either a 4½ hp or a 9 hp, single-cylinder De Dion engine, for Delage did not yet have the facilities to manufacture his own engines. Indeed, he had to practise great economy to be able to prepare two 9 hp racing cars, one with a De Dion and one with an Aster engine, for his first competition, the Coupe des Voiturettes, held at Rambouillet near Paris, in November 1906. A week of regularity trials preceded a race which decided the event and, on the fifth day, in pouring rain, one of the Delage cars ran out of road, hit a tree, and was written off. Fortunately, in the race itself, Delage's other driver, Ménard, who held a Delage agency, finished second, five minutes behind the winning Sizaire-Naudin.

The two-cylinder Delages entered in the 1907 Coupe des Voiturettes race were outclassed, and the fame of the firm really started in the following year on the day before the French Grand Prix at Dieppe, when the 1908 Grand Prix des Voiturettes was held over six laps of the 47.74 mile Grand Prix circuit. The date was Monday, 6 July. Among the 47 starters,

Above: the Delage AB 8 model, of which nine different versions were produced from 1910 to 1913. The car was powered by a four-cylinder, 2121 cc engine. The example pictured above is now preserved in the automobile museum at Turin

Delage fielded a team of three cars, two with two-cylinder, 78 × 130 mm De Dion engines, driven by René Thomas and Lucas-Bonnard, and one with a single-cylinder, 100 × 160 mm engine, driven by Albert Guyot, the Delage agent at Orléans. This engine was the work of a brilliant, but somewhat eccentric, engineer called Nemorin Causan. It had four plugs and four valves per cylinder, two flywheels and thermo-syphon cooling; it developed 28 bhp at 2800 rpm. With this car Guyot had an impressive non-stop winning drive at 49.8 mph, finishing ahead of the fastest Sizaire-Naudin, which had to stop to refuel. All the Delages finished, and the team won the regularity prize, Thomas in fifth place driving the first two-cylinder car to finish. Once again, Louis Delage's financial resources had been taxed to the limit, for there was no prize money in those days, and he had to accept what amounted to a bribe from De Dion to say that Guyot's car had a De Dion engine, thus depriving Causan of the credit due to him.

However, business was picking up rapidly and, in 1908, over 300 cars were sold. In 1909, Delage went over to four cylinders with engines made by De Dion or Ballot but was soon building his own four-cylinder, side-valve engines. In 1910, a move was made to new premises at 138 Boulevard de Verdun, the birthplace of all future Delage products. By 1912, Delage was employing 350 men and turning out well over 1000 cars a year; his range of medium-sized 12 to 15 hp cars had both four and six-cylinder, side-valve engines of his own manufacture.

It has been said that his touring cars were as well made as they were conventional, but Delage's racing cars were far from being conventional, this being

particularly true of their valve gear. For the 1911 Coupe de l'Auto voiturette race at Boulogne, he built four 3-litre cars with cylinder dimensions of 80 × 149 mm. The Delage cylinders were cast in pairs, and the 60 mm diameter valves were horizontal on opposite sides of the cylinders and were operated by pushrods and bellcrank rockers from two camshafts in the crankcase, the power output being 50 bhp at 3000 rpm. The pistons were steel, but very light, compression ratio was about 5.2 to 1, connecting rods were tubular and the crankshaft ran on five 90 mm bore ball bearings. The inlet valves were in detachable caps with the valve springs inconveniently in the gas stream. The gearbox was 5-speed, giving 60 mph at 1500 rpm in overdrive top. With a non-stop race in view, the cars were fitted with what must have been record size scuttle tanks, holding 26 gallons of petrol. Another reserve tank held about three gallons of oil.

The 387-mile race was a triumph for Delage, his driver Paul Bablot, winning at 55.2 mph by 1 min 11 secs from Boillot's Peugeot, with René Thomas third in another Delage; Delage won the team prize.

The next Delage racers were full Grand Prix cars. Designed by Léon Michelat, they also had horizontal valves, although these were four per cylinder instead of the two per cylinder on the 1911 cars, and had five-speed gear-boxes, but the engines were more than double the size of the 1911 racers, being of 6.2 litres with four 105 × 180 mm cylinders. Horizontal valves ensured a lower-profile engine in view of the long strokes employed at that time. The rear fuel tank held 43 gallons so that a non-stop run could be made in the 569-mile 1913 French GP at Amiens, for which the three cars built were primarily produced, although only two of them ran, driven by Paul Bablot and Albert Guyot.

The 118 bhp Delages proved to be the fastest cars at Amiens, and Bablot made fastest lap at 76.6 mph, but, when in the lead, Guyot had a puncture and his mechanic, leaping out before the car had stopped, was run over by the rear wheel. The subsequent delay gave the race to Peugot and the Delages were fourth and fifth. In the GP de France at Le Mans a few weeks later, the three Delages had to face strong Mercedes opposition, two modified 1908 GP cars and two cars with experimental six-cylinder, ohc, aircraft-type engines. The race was another Delage triumph, with Bablot first, Guyot second and Pilette, driving a 1908 Mercedes, third. The six-cylinder Mercedes of Salzer finished in fourth place while Duray, in the third of the Delage team cars, finished fifth.

The following year, two of these Delages were driven in the Indianapolis 500-mile race, on an independent basis, by René Thomas and Albert Guyot. Thomas won the race with Guyot third behind Duray's 3-litre Peugeot.

For the 1914 French GP, Delage entered three 4½-litre cars for Bablot, Guyot and Duray, their interesting design including twin overhead cams with desmodromic valves (opened and closed by the cam-shaft), twin carburettors, four-wheel brakes and five-speed gearboxes. Though fast in practice, they were not successful, only Duray completing the course and finishing in eighth place.

During World War I, Delage resources were turned over to making shells and other munitions and, after the war, Delage turned to producing large cars rather than the small medium-powered models on which the company's reputation had been based. The first big post-war Delage was the CO, which had an 80 × 150 mm, 4½-litre, six-cylinder, side-valve engine

Opposite page, above and below: pictured at a recent veteran and vintage race meeting, a Délage, powered by a 1500 cc, in-line 8-cylinder, 170 bhp motor; a 1925 Delage V12—the 1992 cc engine produced 195 bhp at 7000 rpm: very impressive for the time

This page, left: the six-cylinder, 5136 cc Delage type 1 racing car of 1922

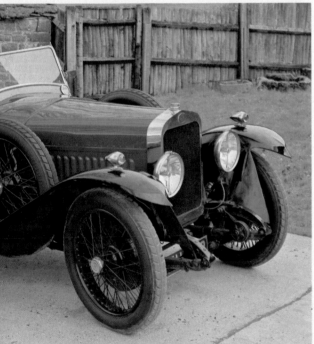

Below left: the DIS of 1924 with coachwork by Kelsch

Below right: in 1929, the famous Delage D8 appeared. It was powered by a straight-eight, 4050 cc engine

Bottom: several versions of the D8 model were available. This is the sporting D8S model capable of 85 mph

with a fixed head. There was a smaller, four-cylinder, 3-litre version called the DO, reputed not to have had front-wheel brakes. In 1921, the CO became the 80 mph CO2 with a pushrod-ohv, twin-plug cylinder head and an output of 88 bhp. The DO was dropped in favour of the DE, still with side valves, but with a smaller 72×130 mm engine of 2.1 litres, and this model was fitted with four-wheel brakes. From the DE in 1923 sprang the famous 14 hp DI series of Delages with pushrod, ohv, 75×120 mm, 2.1-litre engines. These continued from 1923 in conjunction with the GL (Grand Luxe), which replaced the CO2. The GL had a six-cylinder, overhead-camshaft, 95×140 mm, 5.9-litre engine, and was a luxury car also known as the 40/50 in the best Rolls-Royce tradition.

The DI was the most sedate of the 14/40 hp series, and had Rolls-Royce-like, RAF hub-locking arrangements, a 10 ft 6 ins wheelbase, a wide ratio gearbox, magneto or coil ignition on the nearside of the engine, a wide radiator and thermo-syphon cooling. The DIS, of 1924–5, had knock-on Rudge hubs, a 9 ft 9 in wheelbase, a wide-ratio gearbox, magneto ignition on the nearside, a more efficient camshaft and larger valves than the DI, a narrow radiator and thermo-syphon cooling. The DISS of 1925–6 had Rudge hubs, a 9 ft 9 ins wheelbase, a wide-ratio gearbox in 1925 then close ratio in 1926, magneto ignition on the offside necessitating a hole in the block for the high-tension leads to go through, the later camshaft and valves, a narrow radiator and thermo-syphon cooling. The DIS reappeared again in 1927 as the Series 6, the same as before but with coil ignition, a water pump and a close ratio gearbox. The later cars had single-plate clutches.

which were also apt to be a weak feature, but the DI series were generally excellent, reliable cars, not very accelerative but with a high 60 mph cruising speed, a 75 mph maximum speed and impeccable handling. All had 5 main-bearing crankshafts giving 3200 rpm, 4-speed gearboxes and Zenith carburettors.

The 1920s saw the era of the great Delage racing cars. Initially, the emphasis was on hill-climb and sprint cars, beginning, in 1923, with a car which had virtually a prototype DI chassis with larger wheels and tyres and an 85×150 mm bored out CO engine of 5.1 litres with three Zenith carburettors. This was successful at venues such as Mont Ventoux and La Turbie, mainly in the hands of René Thomas, but was also driven by Divo and Benoist. In 1923, a big pushrod V12, $10\frac{1}{2}$-litre, having cylinders with the GL dimensions of 90×140 mm, appeared at Gaillon hill-climb driven by Thomas. Here it broke the record, and, in

1924, Thomas took the land speed record with it at Arpajon at 143.24 mph. This car later became famous at Brooklands in the hands of John Cobb, and is raced today by Johnty Williamson and Cecil Clutton. In 1925, a 5954 cc, six-cylinder car, with a bored-out GL block of 95×140 mm but with twin overhead camshafts and four valves per cylinder, made its debut at Mont Ventoux and, driven by Divo, broke the hill record. This car became known at Brooklands as Delage 1, but it was burned-out at the Phoenix Park races, Dublin, in 1934.

For Grand Prix races, Delage commissioned Plancton to design a 51.3×80 mm, 1995 cc, V12, 4 ohc

Below: by 1935, Delage had been taken over by Delahaye. This is the Delahaye-built Delage D6/70 which used a six-cylinder, 2729 cc engine

Above: the Delage DI 50, with coachwork by Letourneur and Marchand, powered by a 2.5-litre six-cylinder engine

engine developing 110 bhp at 5500 rpm, which was put into a chassis similar to that of Delage 11. It retired when driven by Thomas in the 1923 French GP, but, in 115 bhp form, obtained places in most 1924 Grands Prix. In 1925, the Delages, with supercharged engines developing 195 bhp, recorded wins in the French GP at Montlhéry and the Spanish GP. The Delages were evidently as fast as their chief GP rivals, the P2 Alfa Romeos, with whom, however, they seldom came into direct competition.

1926 saw the advent of the famous and successful Lory-designed straight-eight twin ohc, 1½-litre, five-speed, supercharged Delage, giving 170 bhp at 8000 rpm and 130 mph. The 1½-litre was the last Grand Prix model made by Delage.

The DM series was announced in the summer of 1926, a 3.2-litre with the same cylinder dimensions as the DI, but using six-cylinders. It had the virtues of the DI together with the refinement and flexibility

of a six, and it has been termed the ultimate development of the vintage Delage. The DMS was the high performance version, which differed in quite a number of respects including a more sporting camshaft, larger inlet tract, double valve springs and different gear and back axle ratios, while even con-rods and certain crankshaft dimensions appear to have been different. There was also a short lived DR model, of 2.2 and 2.5 litres, with a side-valve engine.

In 1929, the celebrated 85 mph D8 Delage was announced, a pushrod straight-eight, initially with a 77×109 mm, 4050 cc engine and a chassis destined to be fitted with very exotic bodywork. There were three chassis lengths, the 'S' or 'C' at 10 ft 10 in, the 'N' at 11 ft 8 in and the 'L' at 11 ft 11 in. The 100 mph Grand Sport was introduced in 1932, originally with a 10 ft 3 in wheelbase, but this went up to 10 ft 10 in in 1934. In 1934–5, a completely new and smaller D8 was introduced, the D8 15 of 70×75.5 mm, 2668 cc, with transverse leaf and wishbone independent front suspension, which was also fitted under licence by Studebaker in the USA. This, and some of the 4-litre D8s, had valves divorced from their springs, the link being a rocker mechanism, a design eccentricity with no obvious mechanical advantages. The D6/11 had similar features, and a similar 75×75.5 mm, six-cylinder, 2149 cc engine, just as the original D6 of 1932 had been a six-cylinder version of the D8 of that time. There was also a 1½-litre, 4-cylinder in 1934–6.

By 1935, Delage had been taken over by Delahaye, and as that firm's last competition success had been a rather insignificant best time in the touring class of the Paris-Amsterdam-Paris race of 1898, the sudden racing successes of Delahaye from 1935 onwards must have owed more than a little to Delage know-how. Louis Delage was promptly pensioned off, and lived thereafter in comparative penury.

Delahaye continued the eight-cylinder Delages, which gradually got bigger, with the 79.2×90.5 mm 3591 cc D8 85 of 1935, with normal valve springs, the D8 100 with an 80×107 mm, 4300 cc engine of 1936, and the 'super sports' D8 120 of 1937, which had a shorter wheelbase of 10 ft 10 ins, but this went up to 11 ft 1 in in 1938. Finally, in 1939, came the D8 120 with an 84×107 mm, 4743 cc engine and a Cotal electro-magnetic gearbox.

The later D8 cars were perhaps not quite worthy of the earlier ones, but the six-cylinder, Delahaye-built Delages commendably carried on the DI and DM traditions in the developments of the D6/11, which were the 80×90.5 mm, 2729 cc D6/70 of 1936, the 2.8-litre D6/75 of 1938 and the postwar, 3-litre 'Olympic' D6/3L. These shared similar independent front suspension with the Delahayes, but had hydraulic instead of the Delahaye's cable brakes, and they also shared the excellent Cotal gearbox.

One V12 competition car was built intended for Le Mans, similar to the V12 Delahaye in engine design, but apparently with D6/75 blocks. It never ran at Le Mans, but caught fire soon after the start of the 1938 International Trophy race at Brooklands with tragic results, and was not heard of again. A sports/racing D6 with a 2988 cc engine won the 1938 TT at Donington Park and was second at Le Mans in 1939, but the last Delage racing successes were in 1949–50 with second places at Le Mans and in the GP de Paris with six-cylinder, 3-litre cars.

Delage was absorbed along with Delahaye by Hotchkiss in 1954, and no more cars were made. Louis Delage, who turned to religion in later life, died in 1947, a poor though evidently not unhappy man whose name will undoubtedly live on.   PH

steering-column change of the first Delahaye with wheel steering: the Type 10B of 1901. Shaft-drive was first adopted on a twin-cylinder model in 1907, but chain-drive was continued on the larger cars up to 1911. An L-head mono-block engine was first catalogued in 1908 on the 1.4-litre Type 32. In 1907, all models had two half-elliptic springs at the back shackled to a third inverted transverse spring, as on the contemporary Delaunay-Bellevilles.

By 1907, Delahayes were being made under licence by Protos in Germany, and they entered the English market in 1909, imported by H. M. Hobson of Claudel-Hobson carburettors. In 1909, the makers of the White steam car, of Cleveland, Ohio, abandoned steam and their petrol cars were close copies of the Delahaye design. Their privacy caused mixed feelings in the rue du Banquier, but World War 1 came before any action was taken, and the matter was allowed to drop.

Before the outbreak of war, a novelty introduced by Delahaye was pressure lubrication to the spring shackles, while in England in 1911, Parry Thomas's electric transmission was successfully fitted to the four-cylinder Delahaye belonging to one of Thomas's backers, W. F. Hickman. 1911 saw a notable Delahaye engine introduced by Monsieur Charles. One of the world's first V6s, of 3.2 litres, it was fitted to a car known as the Type 44. The intricate casting had the cylinders at thirty degrees, with two camshafts dealing with three cylinders each; the very compact block measured only thirteen inches in length. Inlet and exhaust passages were cast integral with it, giving the whole the appearance of a large single cylinder. The model was not successful and was discontinued in 1914.

After World War I, Delahaye spent fourteen years producing what motoring historian Michael Sedgwick has described as 'stodgy, dependable and uninteresting cars', and motoring-writer and ex-racing driver John Bolster has said that the vintage Delahaye of 1920–1930 was 'a dull, non-performing vehicle'. As a result of his wartime production experiences, Monsieur Charles, like Citroën and Renault, was attracted to American-style mass production, and also to the standardisation of components amongst manufacturers. Yet Delahaye were early in fitting front-wheel brakes (1921) and carried on their usual extensive and not particularly standardised range: it embraced side-valve, inlet-over-exhaust and ohv, four and six-cylinder engines. For a period, however, they co-operated with Chenard-

Walcker and the FAR Tractor Company, when Delahayes and Chenard-Walckers were almost identical. This attempt to emulate General Motors did not last long. By 1930–31, Delahayes were distinctly unattractive, with American-like ribbon radiators, and they were not selling well in this time when there was a financial depression.

With typical foresight, Monsieur Charles then went on a completely new tack, and Delahaye entered the performance field with the exhibition, at the 1933 Paris Show, of the six-cylinder, push-rod, 3.2-litre Superluxe, with a light chassis, transverse independent front suspension, streamlined bodywork and the choice of a Cotal electromagnetic gearbox, or synchromesh. There was also a four-cylinder, 2150 cc version, with the same cylinder dimensions, and a sports edition of the Superluxe, the 18 Sport.

In 1934, a streamlined and stripped saloon 18 Sport took eighteen world and international class records at Montlhéry, circulating for 48 hours at over 107 mph. Success in the 1935 Alpine Trial bred a 'Coupe des Alpes' model of 3.2 litres and 110 bhp, and, in 1936, the famous competition Type 135 of 3.5 litres was developed from the 130 bhp road-going 135, giving 160 bhp. Meanwhile, in 1935, Delahaye had taken over the Delage company. However, they continued building successful Delage models, and Sport

Top: success in the 1935 Alpine Trial bred this 'Coupe des Alpes' model of 3.2 litres and 110 bhp

Above: developed from the roadgoing type 135, this competition version produced 160 bhp from its 3.5-litre motor. The car pictured above is a 1936 model and belongs to the famous motor-racing personality Rob Walker

Delahayes won eighteen minor sports-car circuit races in France, as well as hill-climbs, and took fifth place at Le Mans.

In 1936, Delahaye entered the big league of sports-car racing with the 135 'Competition', breaking the Ulster TT lap record for all time, and being beaten only by a Type 57S 'tank' Bugatti in the French GP sports-car race; the Bugatti was followed home by no less than four Delahayes. Although beaten by a super-charged 2900A Alfa Romeo in the Belgian 24 Hours Race, Delahayes filled the first five places at the three-hour Marseilles GP sports-car race at Miramas.

In 1937, Delahayes were second and third to a Type 57S Bugatti at Le Mans, won the twelve-hour sports-car race at Donington Park and were third in the Mille Miglia to two 2900A Alfa Romeos. One of the drivers of the latter Delahaye was Laury Schell, husband of Lucy O'Reilly Schell, who had won the Coupe des Dames for Delahaye in the 1935 Monte Carlo Rally and who started the 'Ecurie Bleu' Delahaye racing-stable. 1937 saw a Delahaye win the Monte Carlo Rally outright.

In the winter of 1936–7, Monsieur Charles asked his chief engineer, Jean-François, to design a car suitable for both sports-car and GP racing. The result was the Type 145, which had a de Dion back axle and a 4½-litre, V12, pushrod engine with three camshafts, dual ignition and three carburettors. The engine developed 245 bhp at 5000 rpm. One of these cars, driven by René Dreyfus, won 200,000 francs presented by the French government by averaging 91.07 mph for 200 kilometres at Montlhéry. Jean-Pierre Wimille earned a similar sum by averaging 91.13 mph in a Type 59 GP Bugatti, over the same road-cum-track circuit. In 1938, on the small twisting Pau circuit, Dreyfus won the Pau GP in a Type 145, an Ecurie Bleu entry, from the 425 bhp, V12, 3-litre GP Mercedes W154 of Caracciola/Lang, which had to stop to refuel, whereas the Delahaye did not. On fast circuits, the 145 was out-classed as a GP car, although it later had a proper single-seater body in contrast to the Pau car, which actually had doors. A handful of touring V12s were sold, these being the single-ignition Type 165s. In the same year of 1938, Type 135 Delahayes won Le Mans and the Monte Carlo and Paris–Nice rallies, while a V12 sports car was 4th in the Mille Miglia.

After concentrating on the production of trucks

during World War II, Delahaye were quickly back to car production in 1946, and, between 1946 and 1950, the Type 135s won several races such as the GP de Frontières and the Comminges GP. The post-war sports model was known as the 135M. In 1947, new cars were factory-styled by Philippe Charbonneaux, and in 1948 the new Type 175 appeared with a seven, instead of the traditional four, main-bearing engine, this being a big, six-cylinder 4½-litre. A de Dion back axle was featured, and this was the first Delahaye with left-hand drive. Coachbuilders continued building special bodies on Delahayes, some of them being in execrable taste.

Although a 175S sports model won the 1951 Monte Carlo rally, the 175 and its sister 180 model were not successful, being heavy and costly to run, and they were dropped in favour of the Charbonneaux-styled Type 235 in 1951, a 135 with the engine uprated to give 152 bhp. Monsieur Charles was now assisted by his son, Raymond, but sales dropped dramatically and, after production of a Jeep-like vehicle, Delahaye were taken over in 1954 by Hotchkiss, when car production ceased and only trucks were made. Not long afterwards, the new company was taken over by the Brandt organisation and renamed Hotchkiss-Brandt, and the honoured name of Delahaye was dropped altogether after 1956.　　　　PH

THE CAR MAGNIFICENT

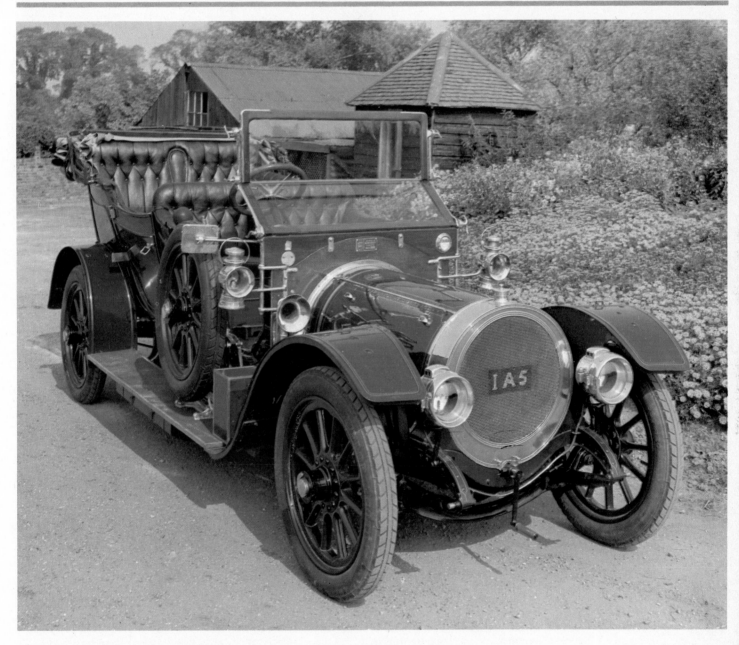

MOST NEW CARS ARE LAUNCHED with a certain amount of doubt as to whether or not they will succeed, but when Delaunay-Belleville of Saint-Denis announced their first motor car at the 1904 Paris Salon, the motoring press received it with an almost unprecedented enthusiasm.

Delaunay-Belleville had already achieved tremendous success as manufacturers of locomotive and marine boilers and steam engines (Louis Renault served an apprenticeship with them in the mid-1890s), but this hardly seemed sufficient justification for such eulogies as L. Baudry de Saunier heaped on it in the January 1905 issue of *La Vie Automobile*: 'Announcing some cars which bear one of the greatest

names of French industry. They are thus born with the weighty obligation of being equal to the renown of their family. I have real pleasure in confirming that the famous factory of Saint-Denis can, without demur, recognise them as its daughters'.

Designer of the new cars was Marius Barbarou, formerly with Clément and Benz who, at the age of 28, was now given the task of creating a range of vehicles suited to the exacting requirements of a select clientele who demanded absolute comfort combined with elegance and mechanical perfection.

Three models constituted the Delaunay-Belleville range for 1905: a live-axle 16 hp, with a top speed of 40 mph, a 24 hp with chain final drive and a 45 mph

Above: trademark of the early Delaunay-Belleville cars was their distinctive rounded radiator. Like so many French motor manufacturers operating during the early part of this century, Delaunay-Belleville were also makers of railway rolling stock

Above: a touring Delaunay-Belleville of 1924. Its four-cylinder engine was capable of pushing the car along at a respectable 85 mph. At this time the company was producing a number of models, including 10/12 and 14/16 hp four-cylinder versions and three six-cylinder models ranging from a 14/16 hp to the massive 40/50 hp of 8 litres

maximum and a 40 hp, again chain driven, which could attain 55 mph. All were four-cylinder models, and were probably the first cars to feature pressure lubrication of the crankshaft though, as Delaunay-Belleville themselves were quick to point out, the idea itself was not new as they had patented it in 1897 and had already used it on steam engines of from 10 to 6800 bhp.

The design of the cars was full of such ingenious features; for example, the bodywork could be lifted from the chassis simply by undoing four bolts, while the chassis frame itself had 'hermetically sealed' undershields running the entire length to protect the mechanism from road grit and dust. The makers were obviously worried that the cars might be driven too quickly, so they ensured that shortage of brakes would never be a problem; the brake cheeks of both brakes were hollow, and were water fed from a two gallon tank, and steam escape orifices were provided to the water spaces in the event of long hills!

The hallmark of the Delaunay-Belleville was its circular radiator and bonnet, which, it was said, commemorated the company's long association with boilers.

Right from the start, the Delaunay-Belleville was established as one of the world's leading quality makes; at the Paris Salon in December 1905, M. Delaunay-Belleville showed his new triple phaeton to President Loubet who was reportedly highly impressed and, by 1906, the company had gained its most illustrious client, the Czar of Russia, who had bought one of the new 40 hp sixes.

Delaunay-Belleville were the first French company to market a six-cylinder model seriously; alongside the 40 they introduced a massive 70 hp model which, though it was not listed for either the 1907 or 1908 seasons, once more became available in 1909 and continued in limited production until 1912. It was this model which subsequently gained the designation Type SMT (Sa Majesté le Tsar) because of the Russian Emperor's predilection for it; he bought one of the very last 70s to be built in 1912, a vast limousine with a clerestory roof.

In 1909, the Czar ordered yet another Delaunay-Belleville, but the head of the Imperial garages (presumably M. Kégresse, who later designed the Citroën half-track), laid down that the car must be capable of being started from the driving seat in absolute silence. The car weighed 4 tons in running order and the problem of silent starting was overcome by using an engine-driven compressor pump which supplied air at 100 lb per sq in to a pressure reservoir.

This device, known as the Barbey starter, was available on all models from the end of 1910.

Between 1906 and 1914, the company produced a bewildering variety of four and six-cylinder models; the make was handled in Great Britain by the Burlington Carriage Co of Oxford Street, London, who had previously been associated with De Dietrich. The cars were sent over from France by sea and, unless the customer had specified a particular coachbuilder, the chassis were shipped to Aberdeen, where Shinnie Brothers, a subsidiary of Burlington, built the body and returned the completed vehicle to London by rail.

One of the more spectacular orders received by the London agency was for an open touring six-cylinder 40 hp for the Maharajah of Cooch Behar.

Around 1909, the agency was acquired by three former Burlington employees, Delaney, Maysmith and Carroll; Burlington closed down soon after.

Increasingly, it seems, Delaunay-Bellevilles were imported into England already fitted with Continental coachwork; the coachbuilders most associated with the marque were the Belgium company of D'Ieteren Frères. Their limousine laundaulette was said to be a popular type of body in conjunction with a noise-less chassis; on the 26 hp Delaunay-Belleville, this style cost £900 complete, a price roughly halfway between Napier and Rolls-Royce.

In 1919, Barbarou left Delaunay-Belleville to join Lorraine-Dietrich and, from that point, the marque's old quality began a gentle decline. Post-war models initially retained the round radiator and bonnet, though the lines of the radiator were softened and given a V front. New models were beginning to make their appearance, there was even an uncharacteristic venture into the voiturette field with a 10 hp four, which was probably the most expensive light car on the market, but more typical was the P4B 15.9 hp four of 1922, with its overhead-camshaft engine.

The pre-war 20 and 30 hp sixes remained in production until 1927, gaining four-wheel brakes in 1923. New 16/60 and 14/40 hp four-cylinder models appeared in 1926, with pushrod-operated overhead-valves; an indication of the diminishing standards of Delaunay-Belleville was the use of a central gear lever on the new models instead of the traditional right-hand change. Gone, too, was the circular radiator, replaced by a conventional cooler of no individuality.

A 3180 cc, 21 hp six was introduced in 1928, with servo-assisted braking on the front wheels, and transmission operated by the pedal and the handbrake acting on the rear wheels. An unpleasing variant of this model appeared in 1929 under the designation 20/65 hp, with side instead of overhead valves. It lasted just a year in production, and was then replaced with the 25/75 hp, 3619 cc ohv six. *The Autocar* could find nothing kinder to say than: 'The car has a particularly solid appearance, is typical of a vehicle of French manufacture, and should prove extremely durable'.

The crowning insult came in 1931, when 4 and 4.5-litre Continental engines imported from America were offered in the six-cylinder chassis; they were, it was said, cheaper and quieter than the French product. By the late 1930s, the company was offering a 2.3-litre six, with styling reminiscent of the contemporary Mercedes-Benz 230; this model was revived briefly after World War II, up-dated with a new radiator grille and a Cotal electrically operated gearbox. However, France in the 1940s was hardly the right milieu for even a lack-lustre Delaunay-Belleville such as this one, and the marque which had once borne the slogan 'The Car Magnificent' ceased production in 1950; its factory was acquired by a cyclecar maker. DBW

BICYCLES, MOTOR CYCLES AND FIRE ENGINES

The Dennis Company has led a varied career. The huge trucks and fire-engines of today are a far cry from the early days of bicycles and Light Doctors' Cars

THE BROTHERS JOHN AND RAYMOND DENNIS began building bicycles in 1895, using the branches of an old pear tree behind their shop in Guildford, Surrey, as an assembly line. They must have been well made, those Speed King bicycles, for the mighty Rover company took out a licence to copy some of the design features on their own products.

In 1898, they fitted a De Dion engine into a tricycle, and were soon marketing similar machines, as well as a convertible quadricycle, but their first venture into motor cars proper was made late in 1899, when they showed two Speed-King Light Doctors' Cars at the National Cycle Show which was held at the Crystal Palace in London.

Priced at £135, the cars were of the petrol/oil type, and intended especially for doctors, surveyors, etc, for hard daily work on country roads. Apart from their 3½ hp De Dion motor, which was air-cooled and mounted at the rear, the cars were built by the brothers; three-speed gearing was fitted, giving speeds of 4, 10 and 20 mph—on the hill-climbing gear, even the steepest of hills could be easily mounted with two persons aboard.

It seems, however, that the Light Doctors' Car did not go into production for, at the next year's National Show, only motor-tricycles and quadricycles (plus the Speed-King Light Pony Carriage, the outcome of a long period of personal knowledge of Shetland ponies) were on show. The tricycles were, it was claimed, capable of covering the extraordinary distance of 30 miles in the hour, and could be relied on for ten years. By 1901, the tricycles could be fitted with the 3½ hp De Dion engine to give a 40 mph top speed (over three times the British legal speed limit) but, alongside them, the company was now building two light cars of up-to-the-minute specification, an 8 hp single fitted with a special regulator which reduced noise to a minimum when standing still, and a 12 hp twin. The 8 hp used a De Dion power unit; the 12 seems to have had an Aster engine. Tubular frames and shaft drive were features common to both cars, which were fitted with three-speed gearboxes.

At the 1903 Motor Show, held at the Crystal Palace, Dennis showed another new Aster-engined model, the 16/20 hp four-cylinder which cost 500 guineas in chassis form. There were now two 12 hp models, the 12/14 hp Aster and the 12 hp De Dion; the De Dion version was available as a hansom cab, and this Dennis model was therefore one of the very first cars to be built as a taxi.

Around this time, the company produced its sole venture into the sports-car field, a lone 40 hp Simms-engined Gordon Bennett-type racer, and the old tricycles and quadricycles, which had outlived nearly all their contemporaries, were pensioned off.

In 1904, Dennis introduced what was to be their hallmark—a worm-drive back-axle, fitted in the interests of silent running.

The 1905 Tourist Trophy race saw two virtually standard 14 hp tourers finishing in 16th and 18th places, while in March 1906 a 20 hp Roi des Belges phaeton took part in an Automobile Club-observed run which covered 4000 miles; its performance earned it the Dewar Trophy for 1907, and replicas of the car were offered for sale to the public.

The Dennis Company was now moving into higher price brackets and in 1906 White & Poppe engines of 30/35 and 24/30 hp were fitted for the first time; this make of power unit was soon standardised. A two-model policy was pursued in 1908 with 20 hp and 35/40 hp fours, then in 1909 four new models—18, 24, 28 and 40 hp—replaced them, only to be supplanted themselves the following year by three new cars.

Only the 40 hp remained in production; the new models were the larger 18 and 24 hp cars and a monstrous 60 hp six-cylinder. All these models were swept away at the end of 1911, except for the 20 (the old 18 hp renamed) and the 24.

These two models, augmented by a 1913 15.9 hp, remained in production until 1914, and the outbreak of World War I. Dennis had already established a thriving commercial-vehicle business, especially noted for its fire engines, and these were so popular that private cars were not reintroduced after the Armistice.

However, Dennis did retain one tenuous link with their automotive beginnings: during the 1920s they regularly advertised their motorised lawn mowers in the august pages of *The Autocar*.   DBW

Above: a far cry from the huge trucks and commercial vehicles associated with the name of Dennis today is this 1909 Dennis four-seater tourer. In 1909, four new models, the 18, 24, 28 and 40 hp, were introduced, but were replaced by three new models the following year

As gracious in defeat as in victory

CONSIDERED BY MANY as the greatest racing driver the United States has ever known, Ralph de Palma was indeed one of the most successful. Over a 27-year period, he participated in approximately 2800 speed events and won over 2500 of them. Above all else, he was a pleasant, friendly man, always willing to offer advice and assistance, even to rival teams. A true sportsman, he accepted defeat with grace.

De Palma, one of four brothers, was born in Southern Italy in 1883, and taken to the United States by his parents ten years later. He soon forgot his native tongue and became accepted as an American. He began racing in 1908, a time when dirt and board-track racing was prevalent—road-racing was then outlawed and Indianapolis had not been built. From the start, he was a success and was recognised as the leading dirt and board track driver. Soon he was competing in sand races, on closed road tracks and, in 1911, the first Indianapolis 500-mile race.

The 1912 Indianapolis 500-mile race is often cited as an example of de Palma's sportsmanship. Driving his sleeve-valve Mercedes Grey Ghost, de Palma seemed an easy winner when a piston collapsed with only ten miles to run. Running on three of its four cylinders, the Mercedes was nursed round while second man Joe Dawson's National began to make up its five-lap deficit. As de Palma completed his 198th lap, Dawson was only three laps behind and racing at twice the speed. Three-quarters of a lap later the Mercedes coughed its last and de Palma said to his riding mechanic, Australian Rupert Jeffkins: 'I guess it's time to start walking, and we might as well take the car with us'.

As the pair pushed their heavy Mercedes, the National completed its three laps to win the victor's laurels. However, the crowd's cheering was shared between Dawson and de Palma, who took defeat like a man. Utterly exhausted, de Palma went up to his young rival, shook his hand and warmly congratulated him.

Also that year, de Palma had his most serious accident. In the 1912 Grand Prize road race near Milwaukee, he crashed on the last lap, while attempting to overtake a rival, Caleb Bragg. Seriously injured and bleeding, he was brought back to race headquarters in the ambulance. On being taken out, he saw press reporters and whispered to them: 'Boys, don't forget that Bragg wasn't to blame. He gave me all the road'.

In 1914, the French Peugeot team arrived in America for the Indianapolis 500-mile race and team manager W. F. Bradley told de Palma that his drivers didn't know the turns well. De Palma said to them: 'Just tuck yourself in behind me for a few laps and I will show you the best place to enter the bends'.

De Palma's most meritorious victory came in 1914. The previous year he had been appointed captain of the Mercer team, but the American cars were frail and it was only early in 1914 that they began to show reliability as well as speed. The Vanderbilt Cup race, run around the roads at Santa Monica, was to be held at the end of February and, for this event, Mercer executives

Above: Ralph de Palma, hero of America's early racing history – he won 2500 of the 2800 events he entered

Left: de Palma's Fiat S74 in action during the 1912 French Grand Prix

went behind de Palma's back and hired Barney Oldfield. This so upset de Palma, who was not consulted until after the deal, that he resigned on the spot.

What car was he to race? His old friend E. J. Schroeder brought de Palma's Mercedes Grey Ghost out of retirement, hastily prepared it and rushed it to California where practice had already commenced. De Palma's practice laps were 40 secs slower round the 8-mile circuit than Oldfield or the other Mercer drivers; prospects looked poor.

In the early stages, de Palma was well out of the reckoning, but steady and reliable driving was rewarded with fifth place as the race progressed. Then the leader crashed; Oldfield had to stop for oil and tyres; a broken propeller shaft eliminated another leader. De Palma and the Mercedes Grey Ghost were ahead! On the 25th lap, with ten to go, Oldfield's superior speed told, and he retook the lead. He didn't draw away, however, as de Palma used every tactic in the book to remain in contact, slipstreaming to great advantage.

De Palma had not made a pit-stop, but he could see Oldfield would probably have to, as his wild driving was causing the tyres to wear rapidly. On one lap, knowing that Oldfield was watching him, de Palma slowed as if to come into the pits. Oldfield felt that the race was now his, reckoned he had a comfortable lead and, to play safe, decided to stop next time round for new tyres. As he sat in the pits the old Grey Ghost raced by into the lead. De Palma had never stopped; he had eased off to lure Oldfield into thinking he had! Try as he might, Oldfield could not reduce the deficit and had to be content with second place.

European racegoers saw de Palma compete in the 1912 and 1914 French Grands Prix. Driving a Fiat, he was disqualified on the first occasion owing to his being unfamiliar with the refuelling regulations. In 1914, as a member of the Vauxhall

team, gearbox trouble put him out. He also went to Germany (only a few days before the outbreak of World War I) to purchase a new Mercedes. He took it back to the United States where he won several important races, including the 1915 Indianapolis 500-mile race.

In 1919, working at Packard, de Palma developed the well known Liberty engine; also, with a 15-litre V12 Packard, he smashed the measured-mile record at Daytona Beach at 149.87 mph. The following season saw de Palma become a member of the French Ballot team. After some American events, he raced for the team in the 1921 French Grand Prix at Le Mans, finishing second to his compatriot Jimmy Murphy in the American Duesenberg. However, Ballot and de Palma had their disagreements, one of them concerning the French race.

De Palma and his nephew Peter de Paolo, his riding mechanic, devised a system of which Ballot disapproved. Not quite automatic transmission—de Palma arranged a neat gearchange manoeuvre whereby he would signal and declutch while de Paolo changed gear! This enabled de Palma to keep both hands on the steering wheel and, perhaps, gain a fraction of a second here and there. Ballot happened to witness these actions and insisted the gear lever be moved to the right-hand side, out of de Paolo's reach.

Back in the United States, de Palma continued racing until 1934, still winning and establishing records although well into his 40s. He drove for Duesenberg, Packard and Miller in major races and then concentrated on 'exhibition' races on the smaller tracks, such as those on which he had started his career. He also performed record-breaking and endurance trials for Chrysler.

The depression of the 1930s, however, meant that it was no longer profitable to race and, at the age of 51, de Palma finally retired. He became a consultant engineer to the Mobil Oil Co and was busily employed by them until his death in 1956. He was 73.   MK

FINANCED IN BRITAIN, BUILT IN FRANCE

'ALTHOUGH THE DERBY IS A FRENCH CAR,' commented *The Autocar* in 1930, 'it is built under British control and with British capital, a somewhat unusual thing in these days.'

However, there was nothing unusual about the marque's origins, for the company had been founded at Courbevoie, Seine, in 1921, just one of the dozens of tiny cyclecar makers which were struggling for a share of the post-war market. Its initial offering was a voiturette with an American-built vee-twin motor-cycle engine, but this was soon replaced by a Chapuis-Dornier engine, and the car became virtually a carbon copy of the successful 5cv Citroën. It was cheap, too, and the English concessionaires could afford to sell the two-seater at £195 in 1923, only £30 more than the cost of the Austin Seven.

Somehow the marque failed to catch on in England, although one of the models at the 1923 Olympia Show did give a promise of where the marque's future lay. This was the 9 hp Sports, with wire wheels and a British-built body, costing £275 complete; a special racing version had already appeared in the 1923 200 miles Race at Brooklands.

In 1927, the car was being sold on its sporting merits in England, under the name Vernon-Derby, by its new agent, Vernon Balls, who had forsaken his originally chosen vocation (of veterinary surgeon) for motor cars. By now, the 8 hp Derby had gained a four-speed gearbox instead of the three-speed unit originally fitted, plus brakes on all wheels. Despite the improvements, the price remained at £275.

The agency passed to Morgan Hastings Limited, of Berkeley Street, London, in 1928, although the Vernon-Derby name was retained for a while. Three models were now available, the original 9 hp sports, plus two new models, the side-valve 1.5-litre sports and the 14 hp. Both had proprietary six-cylinder power units. Another new model appeared in 1929, replacing the side-valve 1.5-litre. This was the 12 hp six, which had a smaller power unit than its predecessor and, again, was a side-valve unit.

The sixes were sporty rather than sports cars; they were generally fitted with two-seater or sportsman's coupé coachwork, although at the 1930 London Motor Show a rather handsome sports two-seater on the larger six-cylinder chassis (increased in size to 16 hp, with a swept volume of 1847 cc) had styling similar to that of the contemporary Bugatti.

Around this time, the marque became seriously involved in motor sport: racing driver Douglas Hawkes had brought a 1500 cc front-wheel-drive Miller racing car over to France, and this, usually handled by Mrs Gwenda Stewart (sister of Glubb Pasha, and later Hawkes' wife) was campaigned as the Derby-Miller. Part publicity-raiser, part test-bench, the car came to incorporate more and more Derby parts over the years.

In 1930, Mrs Stewart took the 1.5-litre class record at Montlhéry, covering a mile at 118.13 mph; the engine was later bored out to 1.7 litres, in which form Mrs Stewart, in 1934, set up a record lap of Montlhéry at 147.79 mph, which stood for five years.

A second 1500 cc racer to bear the Derby name came in 1935, this was the Derby-Maserati, with a supercharged, twin-overhead-camshaft Maserati power unit in a chassis with independent suspension all round. It did not enjoy the success of its predecessor, but still survived in 1974, making occasional appearances at vintage events.

Derby's last production cars were unusual, too. In 1931 came the 12/50, with all-round independent suspension again and front-wheel drive.

Two years later, it was joined by a front-drive, 2-litre V8 model with a similar chassis layout, but this time costing £525 before coachwork was added. Both cars had an interesting forecast of future practice in the positioning of gear and handbrake levers, which protruded through the dashboard.

Gwenda Stewart competed at Le Mans with the V8 in 1934 and 1935, but retired on both occasions.

The front-wheel-drive models, plus an obscure rear-driven Meadows-engined car, were the last new models to be produced by Derby, which abandoned car manufacture in 1936. DBW

Below: the Derby company is remembered mostly for its sporting cars. Founded in 1921, the concern continued to build cars for another fifteen years. Typical of their products is this 1928 sports model which used an 1100 cc, four-cylinder, Chapuis-Dornier engine

IN 1928, WALTER CHRYSLER was riding high. After only four short years of manufacturing, he had risen to third place in the American motor industry, and now he was ready to break into a new sector of the market. A new 3.2-litre, side-valve six was designed to compete in a lower price range than the Chrysler, selling under the marque name of De Soto.

In general appearance, the De Soto resembled the contemporary Chryslers; its 21.6 hp engine was mounted on rubber insulators to reduce vibration, and had full force-feed lubrication. There were hydraulic brakes on all four wheels and, from its chromium-plated ribbon-radiator to its rear-mounted spare wheel, the De Soto represented the most up-to-date motor-engineering practice.

That price was as low as £295 in England for a two-seater with wood wheels; the success of the venture was shown by first-year sales of around 90,000.

A second De Soto model appeared in 1930, a 3.5-litre straight-eight which, at a basic price of £398, was the lowest priced eight-cylinder car in the world. The bodies were bolted to the chassis to form a rigid unit, and among the standard features were Lockheed four-wheel hydraulic brakes and a downdraught carburettor.

However, the depression hit the De Soto's market hard. Sales dropped to 26,000 in 1932, even though the cars were probably better value than ever. Indeed, the De Soto name vanished from the British market around 1931 and, during the 1930s, cars which were sold as De Sotos in America appeared under the Chrysler banner in England.

The 1933 De Sotos (sold as the 20/63 hp Chrysler Richmond and Mortlake in Britain) featured all the Chrysler innovations like two-point 'floating power' engine-suspension, a double-drop girder truss chassis,

and a three-speed manual transmission.

In 1934, of course, De Sotos followed the Chrysler Airflow line with a 4-litre, six-cylinder model, sold in England as the Croydon. However, this appeal to the air-minded went largely unheeded and, for 1936, a more conventional, V-bonnetted styling was adopted. Overdrive was an option on the De Soto Airflows, and later became available on the conventional models as well. Unusual for American cars, 12-volt lighting and starting systems were used.

1936 saw a swing away from the Airflow look, and the adoption of a vertical dummy radiator grill and a rear-hinged alligator bonnet.

By 1939, the cars had acquired independent front suspension and a steering-column gear-shift, as well as a choice of two six-cylinder power units. In 1941, the

CHRYSLER IN DISGUISE

De Soto cars were introduced by Chrysler, to compete in a lower price range

Vacumatic, semi-automatic transmission became available as an option.

After World War II, the De Soto line gained the full-width 'dollar grin' styling fashionable among American cars. The first really new models appeared in 1949, when there were two ranges, the S14 de luxe and custom with 236.7 cu in, L-head, six-cylinder engines and the smaller SP20 Diplomat for export only.

Custom models featured, as standard, Tip-Toe hydraulic gear shifting, in conjunction with Gyrol Fluid Drive; this was optional on the de luxe versions.

Apart from revised styling, the 1951 range was broadly similar, though the stroke was enlarged, increasing the swept volume to 250.6 cubic inches.

The 1952 range was little changed, except for the addition of the new Series S17 Firedome V8 'hemi-head' engine. By 1953, the new V8s were outselling the old sixes, by around two to one.

The power output of the V8 was boosted from 160 to 170 bhp in 1954, and the Firedome was now selling seventy per cent of total De Soto production.

The year 1955 saw a shake-up in the De Soto range, which, once again, underwent styling changes. A new, higher-priced version of the Firedome, the S21 Fireflite, was announced; though it had the same chassis and 291-cubic inch V8 engine as the Firedome, its power output was 200 bhp against the older model's 185. Now, only export markets could buy the six-cylinder De Soto, for it was only available on some Diplomat models, while the S26 Diplomat and Diplomat custom were based on the Plymouth Six Plaza and Belvedere.

The new look 'flight sweep' styling was adopted on all Chrysler models and resulted in an upswing in the group's sagging sales; De Soto, it seems, benefited less than Chrysler and Plymouth. For 1956, a new top-of-the-range model, the Adventurer, was introduced.

The S24 Fireflite range featured push-button automatic transmission as standard; this was an option on the S23 Firedome models. The Diplomat models for 1956 had a choice of 125 bhp, six-cylinder Power-Flow or 187 bhp, V8 Hy-Fire power units, with a less potent V8 available in export markets. In the following year, Diplomats acquired the option of overdrive and Power Flite automatic transmission, while the Diplomat Custom V8 featured Torque Flite automatic transmission.

However, the success of the 1957 season was the new lower priced FireSweep V8 range which, by the end of the year, represented 35 per cent of the marque's total production.

De Sotos were becoming more and more like their Plymouth brethren, a fact which was realised by the formation of the Plymouth-De Soto division of the Chrysler corporation in 1959.

In November 1960, Chrysler announced that no more De Soto cars would be made and yet another famous motoring name passed into history. DBW

Above: a subsidiary of the giant Chrysler Corporation, De Soto produced cars from 1928 until 1960. This is the 1928 De Soto Six which featured a six-cylinder, 3.2-litre engine

ITALIAN PRECISION WITH BRUTE FORCE

After a disastrous start, the name De Tomaso is now associated with luxury high-performance cars combining Italian styling and American engineering

Below: the first of De Tomaso's road-going cars was the four-cylinder, 1500 cc Ford-engined Vallelunga. Originally the car was an open two-seater, but in 1965 Giugiaro produced this attractive coupé design

Bottom: the car that established De Tomaso as a serious threat to other luxury high-performance car manufacturers: the Mangusta

THE MOTOR INDUSTRY HAS ATTRACTED some bizarre characters in its short history, but few stranger, or more ingenious, than Alessandro de Tomaso, the Argentinian racing driver turned car manufacturer. For many years he seemed destined to emulate the famous Bucciali brothers of the twenties and thirties who designed magnificent cars to be exhibited at motor shows, but seldom deigned to build one for a customer.

De Tomaso was born in Argentina, but he emigrated to the United States in his youth and there he met and married Isabel Haskell, a wealthy American girl. Together they took up motor racing, concentrating on Sports Car Club of America road racing, usually with OSCA cars. They sometimes partnered each other in long distance races with moderate success and, in the late 1950s, they came to Europe to race their small capacity OSCAs. They naturally gravitated to Modena in Italy where the OSCA was built by the Maserati brothers and, in 1959, de Tomaso decided to set up as a racing-car manufacturer. He took a small workshop in Modena and, after dabbling with small-capacity, single-seaters, threw himself in at the deep end by

developing a Formula One car for the new 1½-litre Formula which commenced in 1961. He turned to his friends at OSCA for the engine, using their twin-overhead-camshaft, four-cylinder, 1500 cc engine, but it was really only a sports-car engine and it lacked the power even of the four-cylinder Coventry Climax engine. He switched to the Alfa Romeo engine but this again was a four-cylinder, twin-overhead-camshaft production Giulietta engine which was not competitive. The car followed contemporary Cooper lines and was neatly made but, although competent drivers such as Nino Vaccarella, Giorgio Scarlatti, and Roberto Businello drove the cars, they seldom managed to finish or even put up a good performance.

Rather than buy a competitive engine from another manufacturer, de Tomaso began to develop his own Formula One engine, a flat-8, 1½-litre unit. This duly appeared in late 1963 but, after a brief practice appearance, it was quietly put away, never to re-appear. This set the pattern for de Tomaso, who threw himself energetically into some new venture only to lose interest if it did not work at the first attempt, and sometimes even before he had finished it.

In the early 1960s, the Italian Grand Prix was usually on the banked circuit, the broken surface of which played havoc with the fragile suspensions of Grand Prix cars. In conjunction with a metallurgist, de Tomaso developed a metal which had a degree of elasticity incorporated, so that, instead of breaking when used in the suspension of a racing car, it would bend, then return to its normal shape. He went to the expense of casting special wishbones before realising that when his suspension arms bent they would alter the steering geometry of the car, and, if the car hit a very bad bump, the chassis would hit the ground. Again the idea was dropped.

When the monocoque-chassis Lotus 25 appeared, de Tomaso decided to go one better than the rivetted aluminium structure of the Lotus and cast his complete Formula One chassis in one unit. The design was completed and the 'bathtub'-type monocoque chassis was cast in magnesium at horrific cost. Undoubtedly, this provided a very stiff chassis, but it allowed no room for alterations if the design was not right first time, so once again the idea was scrapped.

De Tomaso began to turn his thoughts towards road cars and in 1964 he brought out the Vallelunga, an open two-seater which, again, was unconventional. It used a tubular, central-backbone chassis with a British Ford 1½-litre, four-cylinder engine mated to the rear of this chassis, just ahead of the rear wheels; a four-speed rear-mounted gearbox and final drive took the power to the rear wheels. The car featured double-wishbone suspension on all four wheels and disc brakes all round, and it was clothed in a neat, all-enveloping aluminium body. The engine was tuned to give 100 bhp at 6200 rpm and de Tomaso claimed a top speed of 130 mph. Alas, few, if any, were ever sold.

However, de Tomaso persevered with this backbone chassis idea and in 1965 the young body designer Giorgetto Giugiaro, who was working at that time for Ghia, the bodybuilding firm, designed an attractive coupé body for the Vallelunga. This provoked a great deal of attention, and was put into production at the Ghia factory. However, the few people who drove the car reported that the engine transmitted a great deal of vibration through the central backbone, while the rear suspension, mounted partly on the engine/gearbox unit, was insufficiently rigid. Once again, a de Tomaso car disappeared.

De Tomaso decided to carry on with the idea and he designed a bigger version with a tuned Shelby-

Right: from 180 mph sports cars to tiny City cars, De Tomaso has made them all. This is the 500 cc motor-cycle-engined Rowan produced in collaboration with Ghia

Below: the mid-engined De Tomaso 1600 used a transversely mounted, sixteen-valve, 1600 cc Ford BDA engine. The car was never put into serious production

Cobra, Ford V8 engine mid-mounted. American designer Pete Brock drew up an open, two-seater body for the car which was notable for a large aerodynamic spoiler across the tail; this was linked to the fifth gear so that it flattened when running at maximum speed, but was angled downwards in other gears to give extra adhesion at the rear. The idea was to race the car, starting with the Sebring 12-Hours of 1966, but it never competed. However, the idea of a big, mid-engined sports car continued to germinate in de Tomaso's mind and he asked Ghia to design a body for the car. They set Guigiaro to work and he came up with a breathtakingly beautiful body, of classic simplicity, which was the star of the 1966 Turin Show. Mechanically, the car was essentially the same as the Vallelunga in concept, but the big, 4.7-litre Ford V8 gave a claimed 418 bhp (or 506 bhp with fuel injection) and was mated to a five-speed ZF gearbox. Access to the engine bay was via a pair of vast gull-wing

doors, which gave the car a very futuristic appearance.

Initially, the car was known as the Ghia Mangusta (Italian for mongoose), but de Tomaso soon renamed it the De Tomaso Mangusta when he realised that he had a successful production car on his hands.

Things now began to happen for de Tomaso; his wife persuaded her brother, a director of an American firm, Rowan Controls, to take a financial interest in the De Tomaso factory and also to take over Ghia, who were in financial difficulties. The Americans started promoting the car in the USA and, before long, de Tomaso was presented with an order for 300 Mangustas a year from America. A new factory was acquired in Modena and production got under way in 1968. Unfortunately, the Mangusta had a number of design faults: there was too much weight at the rear of the car and it handled badly, while the passenger accommodation was rather claustrophobic. In a bid to solve these problems, de Tomaso acquired the services of Gian Paulo Dallara, the very talented Lamborghini designer, largely because he promised Dallara that he could build a Formula One car.

During the 1960s, de Tomaso had continued to dabble in racing-car design, but nothing ever got to the stage of actually racing. He envisaged an Indianapolis car, then offered an overhead-camshaft version of the Ford V8 to Indianapolis teams, even claiming that Lotus would use his engine, but the special four-cam Ford engine ended that plan. However, he was as good as his word to Dallara and in 1969 the company built a Formula Two car powered by a Cosworth FVA engine which featured a well made monocoque chassis using magnesium bulkheads. Jacky Ickx, Piers Courage and Jonathan Williams raced the car, which proved to be quite competitive, but failed to win a race. Encouraged by the F2 car, de Tomaso decided to build a Formula One car and reached an agreement for private entrant Frank Williams to provide Cosworth DFV, 3-litre engines and enter the car in the 1970 World Championship series. The car began to perform quite creditably in the hands of Piers Courage, who finished third in the Silverstone International race but, during the Dutch Grand Prix, Courage crashed heavily and was killed.

On the production front, Dallara decided that the best thing to do with the Mangusta was to redesign it completely; so it eventually appeared as the Pantera with a completely new body and revised chassis and suspension. The Pantera proved to be a much better car and was well received by the motoring press and customers alike. Not content with the success of the Pantera, de Tomaso also built a city car, the Rowan, powered by a 500 cc motor-cycle engine, the Deauville, a big front-engined, four-seater reminiscent of a Jaguar XJ6 and the De Tomaso 1600, a transverse, mid-engined Ford BDA-powered coupé using Vallelunga suspension, which many people claimed was a copy of the Fiat X1/9. None of these cars ever got into serious production.

The Ford Motor Company began to show a great deal of interest in the Pantera which they envisaged as a successor to the virtually stillborn GT40 road car. They already supplied standard Ford 5-litre V8 engines for the car and eventually de Tomaso agreed to sell both his company and Ghia to Ford. In 1974, Ford were producing the Pantera in Italy and using the Ghia studios for advanced design work, while de Tomaso had the sales franchise on the Pantera in most parts of the world apart from the USA. He was also free to build special versions of the Pantera for racing or road use and to develop new de Tomaso designs in the future for both racing and production purposes.   MT

PANTERA

For performance, it is said, there is no substitute for cubic inches, and De Tomaso's Pantera (Panther) has 351.7 of them, which makes it a real road burner.

The Pantera is a mid-engined two-seater, built in the classic Italian 'exoticar' style except that, instead of using a multicam, fuel-injected V12, it has an American Ford V8 engine coupled to a German ZF five-speed gearbox. The V8 gives away hardly anything to its thoroughbred counterparts in the way of performance and has substantially superior fuel consumption. Where it does lose out is in the sound of its engine: a typical V8 burble instead of the V12 shriek, but, since the Pantera is about two thirds of the price of its high-performance competitors, it is a small price to pay.

Available in two versions, the L and the GTS (a tuned, rather garishly painted, high-performance version), the Pantera also possesses very high standards of roadholding and handling. In fact, there are probably no more than four cars in the world that can out-corner one.

Good roadholding and handling are usually inherent in a mid-engined layout such as this, because the weight distribution is even. Independent suspension, too, is effective.

The Pantera L has a top speed of 162 mph and accelerates to

60 mph in 6.1 secs, while the GTS has a top speed of 170 mph and accelerates to 60 in 5.5 secs.

Both Panteras feature electrically operated windows, an electrically heated rear window and air-conditioning.

ENGINE Front-mounted, water cooled V8. 101.6 mm (4 in) bore × 89 mm (3.50 in) stroke = 5763 cc (351.7 cu in). Maximum power (SAE) 330 bhp at 5400 rpm (L) or 350 bhp at 6000 rpm (GTS); maximum torque (SAE) 380 lb ft at 3400 rpm (L) or 362 lb ft at 4000 rpm (GTS); maximum engine rpm 6100. Cast-iron cylinder block and head; compression ratio 11:1; 5 main bearings. 2 valves per cylinder, operated via pushrods and rockers, by a single

camshaft at the centre of the V. 1 Autolite downdraught four-barrel carburettor.

TRANSMISSION Single dry-plate clutch; ZF 5-speed all-synchromesh gearbox; ratios 1st 2.420, 2nd 1.470, 3rd 1.090, 4th 0.846, 5th 0.705, reverse 2.865:1; cylindrical-bevel, final drive with limited-slip differential. Ratio 4.220.

CHASSIS Monocoque body/chassis unit.

SUSPENSION Front—Independent by wishbones, coil springs, telescopic dampers and an anti-roll bar; rear—independent by wishbones, coil springs, telescopic dampers and an anti-roll bar.

STEERING Rack and pinion.

BRAKES Servo-assisted discs.

WHEELS 7 in × 15 front, 8 in rear.

TYRES 185/70VR15 front, 215/70VR15 rear (L) or G70 × 15 front and H70 × 15 rear.

DIMENSIONS AND WEIGHT Wheelbase 99.02 in; track—front 57.09 in, rear—57.48 in; length 168.1 in; width 72.05 in (L) or 74.80 in (GTS); height 43.31 in; ground clearance 4.72 in; kerb weight 2933 lb; turning circle between walls 39.4 ft; fuel tank capacity 21 gals.

BODY 2-door, 2-seat coupé.

PERFORMANCE Maximum speed 162 mph (L) or 170 mph (GTS); 0–60 mph 6.1 secs (L) or 5.5 secs (GTS). Fuel consumption approx 15 to 17 mpg.

REPUTATION-
THE IMPORTANT FACTOR

IN 1891, IT IS RECORDED, Monsieur Doriot followed the Paris–Brest cycle race in a Peugeot, 'with adventures and vicissitudes which would astound the modern motorist'; that same Doriot was one of Peugeot's principal racing drivers during the 1890s, with several modest successes to his name.

Doriot went into partnership with a Monsieur Flandrin in 1906, building single-cylinder, shaft-drive voiturettes of no special merit, at Courbevoie, Seine; shortly after this, a Monsieur Parant became a partner in the company. As the name Doriot-Flandrin-Parant was too cumbersome for general use, the cars became known as DFP, which French wags rendered as 'Dernière Ferraille Parisienne'(Latest Paris Scrapiron).

The 1.1-litre singles lasted, it seems, until 1910, but were by then quite overshadowed by the firm's four-cylinder models, introduced in 1908 with 2.4 and 2.8-litre Chapuis-Dornier engines, and joined in 1910 by the 10/12 hp, 1.6-litre model, which really established the marque. Further, the 10/12 was the first DFP model to be launched on the British market; the agent was G. A. Lecoq of New Bond Street, already well known as the manufacturer of Vuitton suitcases and trunks.

Lecoq claimed that the DFP had proved in every respect the most successful small car of 1910, and forecast that in 1911 it would be even more phenomenally successful.

Compared with many of its contemporaries, the 10/12 was quite advanced in concept: the valves were enclosed and the propeller shaft worked inside a torque tube. It was, apparently, extremely light, economical on tyres and would do forty miles an hour and 35 miles to the gallon.

Priced at £235, complete with two-seater body, the DFP cost much the same as the better British light cars like the Calthorpe; already, though, there were signs that added performance was becoming a desirable feature, for a 10/14, overbored for extra power, was added for 1911, which also saw a brief and uncharacteristic venture into six big cylinders with a 20/25 model that failed to see the year out.

Lecoq had a single-minded interest in making money, but was obviously more adept at marketing trunks than motor-cars for, by the early part of 1912, the British DFP operation was in urgent need of additional finance.

'We do not sell the DFP by advertising, but by reputation,' claimed Lecoq, who by this time had established a sales and service depot off Hanover Street, and he added optimistically, 'one satisfied owner tells another, and there are no DFP owners who are not satisfied'.

Whether they were satisfied or not, there simply weren't enough DFP owners to make the business viable, for sales were only running at one a month.

Above: W. O. Bentley poses at the wheel of a 1913 DFP. Long before he established the legendary Bentley marque, W. O. became involved in the motor industry as a director of the DFP company and had a great influence on the design of the company's models

534

Lecoq advertised for a director with money to invest. A young man, H. M. Bentley, replied, having decided that the opening would suit his younger brother Walter, who was at that time managing a fleet of Unic taxis at Hammersmith.

So W. O. Bentley came into the business, for £2000, and found that Lecoq was just a sleeping partner, while the other director, Fernie, was 'noisy, bossy and ineffectual'. The DFPs themselves were well made, reliable cars, with above average performance, especially the new 12/15, introduced at the end of 1911, with a 2-litre engine built by DFP. This power unit had three main bearings, with positive lubrication by a pump which also fed the troughs for the splash lubrication of the big ends; it could spin freely up to 2500 rpm, and gave a top speed of 55 mph.

The cars had a future on the British market, thought Bentley, although it was liable to be a short one with Lecoq and Fernie in charge. In April 1912, therefore, H. M. Bentley bought them out for another £2000, and the firm of Bentley and Bentley came into being with far too little working capital but a great deal of confidence.

One sure way of publicising the DFP—and, hopefully, of gaining some extra sales—was to win one of the major speed events. So with a car tuned by Leroux, a mechanic sent over to Bentley and Bentley from the DFP factory at Courbevoie, W. O. Bentley won his class in the June 1912 Aston Clinton hill-climb at record speed.

Later that year, a streamlined single-seat 12/15 set up a new ten-lap record of 66.78 mph at Brooklands. Bentley was anxious to get still more performance from the car, but was limited by the pistons, which could not withstand the high speed. The answer came, by chance, in 1913, when W. O. Bentley visited Doriot at Courbevoie. On the Frenchman's desk stood a novelty paperweight from the Corbin foundry: it was a tiny piston made from aluminium.

Against Doriot's advice, Bentley had a set of 12/15 pistons cast in aluminium alloy, raised the compression ratio and found an immediate improvement in the power output. After much testing to determine the correct weights and clearances for the pistons, Bentley ordered Courbevoie to build an aluminium-pistoned engine for a sporting variant of the 12/15, to be known as the 12/40 Speed Model.

This was not the first time aluminium pistons had been used on a car—Professor A. M. Low, for instance, had fitted them to his Gregoire—but the idea was still extremely novel. The result of using the new pistons in the racing single-seater was phenomenal. At the August 1913 Brooklands meet, the DFP won the Short Handicap at 70.5 mph, and showed itself capable of lap speeds of over 75 mph. Its main rival was the 2-litre Humber driven by W. A. Tuck, which had, up to then, just managed to top the DFP's performance. True to form, the Humber raised the ten-lap figure at Brooklands to 79.63 mph and the half-mile to 85.53 mph.

Bentley and Leroux worked on the Speed Model DFP single-seater, however, fitting it with two spark plugs, and lightening the chassis. After this, just about every record in the book fell to the car, which covered the flying half-mile at 89.7 mph; the Humber retired from the circuits.

Alongside these competition successes, Bentley had built up a reputation for flair in coachwork design: at the 1912 Olympia exhibition, for example, he showed a four-seater tourer, which was, it was claimed, the first-ever car to be panelled in polished aluminium. Even the 'heavy and sluggish' 16/20 hp model had a share in the elegance, for on the same stand was a two-seater coupé limousine on this chassis; painted dark purple, it was panelled in sycamore and upholstered in doeskin.

In June 1914, Bentley entered a 12/40 in the Isle of Man Tourist Trophy race. Apart from its airship-tailed body, it was virtually a standard vehicle, so that its final position of sixth, behind purpose-built 3.3-litre cars in the race, achieved widespread publicity, for seventeen out of the 23 racers taking part failed to

finish the gruelling Isle of Man race.

In mid July appeared the advertisements boasting the 12/40's sporting achievements—in the Caerphilly Hill-Climb and the Porthcawl Speed Trials as well as the TT—but before the expected orders poured in, the Germans upset matters by declaring war. Operations were suspended during the hostilities.

After the Armistice, of course, W. O. Bentley was busy developing his new 3-litre sports car (the prototype was built in the DFP agency's service garage at New Street Mews), but H. M. continued to run Bentley and Bentley with great success during the post-war boom. He made £20,000 in the first year after the Armistice, and drivers were rushing chassis from the factory to the Channel ports to meet demand. When the boom went off the boil, however, Courbevoie went into a rapid decline.

The last competition version of the old 12/40 appeared at Brooklands in the early 1920s; it was owned by Henry Birkin (later one of the most distinguished Bentley drivers) and had a curious Consuta-sewn plywood body, built on the same principle as Saunders-Roe flying-boat hulls.

The basically Edwardian 12/40 and 10/12 lasted until 1923; indeed, the 10/12 was still listed the following year, although a reduction in chassis price from £430 to £325 made it pretty clear that the new agents, Ward & Driskell, who had taken over the Bentley and Bentley concession (and their North Audley Street showrooms) in mid 1923, were just trying to clear unsold stocks.

A new model, the 9.5 hp DF Petite, had appeared in 1922, but wasn't available in Britain until 1923. With an 1100 cc pushrod ohv CIME engine, it was a lively voiturette, akin to the Amilcar. The 1923 Motor Show car was a bright-red cloverleaf three-seater, with mahogany decking, and at a cost of £295 it was passable value for money.

There was one last sporting venture: one of the voiturettes took second place in its class in the 1926 Bol d'Or, and in 1927 a similar model won outright.

But the victory was too late, for in 1926 the factory had closed down for ever.   DBW

Above: in June 1914, W. O. Bentley entered a 12/40 in the Isle of Man TT race. Apart from its airship-tailed body, the DFP was virtually standard and thus its sixth position behind purpose-built racers achieved much publicity for the company

FROM RAILWAY ENGINES TO RACING CARS

The Diatto is probably best remembered as the forerunner of the modern-day Maserati. However, this is not a completely fair image as Diatto themselves made some interesting cars

SOME MOTOR MANUFACTURERS have gone down in history not so much for their own achievements but for the marques that they have spawned: manufacturers such as Mason, Maxwell, Perry, Castro and Diatto of Turin.

Diatto was a railway engineering and iron-founding concern which entered the motor industry sometime between 1904 and 1907, building Clément-Bayards under licence.

The company started out with high hopes: it had a six-model range consisting of 8 hp and 10 hp twins, and 12, 20, 35 and 50 hp fours. Unfortunately, though, there was a recession in the Italian industry soon after the concern had got under way, and savage cutbacks were necessary.

By 1911, only one model, a 15.9 hp four, was being built; a half-hearted attempt to import this model into Britain was made, but lasted only a short while. In fact, the marque's pre-war history was almost totally undistinguished, being relieved only by an eighth place in the 1914 Targa Florio for Rigoletti's car.

In 1919, Gamboni's Diatto took third place in the same event, although this was completely overshadowed by the antics of the winner, André Boillot, who crossed the finishing line backwards in his Peugeot.

Post-war models were a 10 hp and a 20 hp, both with four-cylinder engines, of 1 and 2.7 litres respectively. There was also a brief excursion into the manufacture of Bugatti Type 13s (like Crossley in Britain and Rabag in Germany), one of which won the 1921 Circuit of Brescia, from which the Type 13 took the name 'Brescia Bugatti'.

The little 10 hp was a far more modern design, with an 8.9 hp side-valve engine, featuring pressure lubrication, and a cowled fan to increase the efficiency of the thermosiphon water circulation.

For the 1923 season, Diatto announced a more exciting new model, the 15 hp four, using the 20 hp chassis, but with a 15.9 hp, single-overhead-camshaft, 2-litre engine of great potential, developing 52 bhp in standard guise. At a chassis price of £575, it appealed to the sporting market, and racing versions were soon in action.

Among the most effective tuners of the 15.9 hp Diatto were the Maserati brothers of Bologna. Alfieri Maserati had already driven a tuned, overhead-camshaft, 3-litre Diatto to a number of class wins; in 1924, he entered a modified 2-litre Diatto with twin overhead-camshafts for the Spanish San Sebastian Grand Prix, and made his way to third place before the engine gave out.

Its performance had been convincing enough for Diatto to commission the Maserati brothers to design a proper racing car in the shape of a straight-eight, 2-litre, GP model. It made only one appearance, at the 1926 Italian Grand Prix, where sheared blower bolts forced its retirement. Diatto, in deep financial trouble, gave the car to the Maseratis for further development

work and withdrew from competition for the time being.

The touring range was rationalised in 1923, when the 10 hp model was dropped, and production centred on the 2-litre Model 20 and its derivatives. The ambitious English importing operation collapsed and the agency passed to Cyril Durlacher of Upper St Martin's Lane, London.

In 1924, a short-wheelbase Super-Sports 2-litre became available, with a lightened chassis on which semi-elliptical rear springs replaced the cantilevers; the 1924 London Show car was a real eyecatcher, with a two-seater body painted geranium red. During the same period, the touring model gained a longer wheelbase and four-wheel brakes as standard.

The 1925 range included another new model, the Model 35 3-litre, on the same chassis as the Model 30 2-litre Super-Sports, while the Model 20a 2-litre touring model continued virtually unchanged; indeed, the same range ran on for another four years before closing down, except for a couple of sporting interludes. First, a handful of the straight-eight, GP-type cars were built as road-going sports cars, then in 1927 the four-cylinder, 5-litre 'M Special' was announced, although it seems to have been undistinguished.

The Maserati brothers, however, had more success: the GP straight-eight Diatto was reborn as the 1500 cc Maserati.

So as Diatto died, Maserati was in the ascendant. Had the 2-litre GP car been more successful and had Diatto been adequately financed, the course of motoring history might have been different, who knows! Maybe Diatto would now be a luxury marque and Maserati still a workshop in Bologna. DBW

Above: Diatto began their career as motor manufacturers by producing cars under licence from Adolphe Clément. Pictured is a 1907 Diatto-Clément with team drivers Burzio and Restelli

THE FACTS ABOUT THE DIESEL ENGINE

The diesel engine is traditionally thought of as the motoring industry's heavy-duty work horse. It is reputed to be strong, reliable and economical, but is this really true?

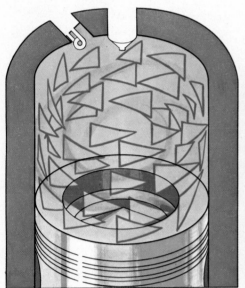

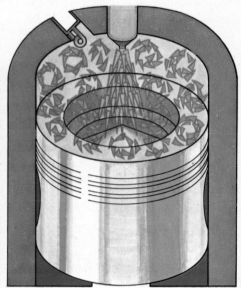

RUDOLF CHRISTIAN KARL DIESEL, born in 1858, the son of an expatriate Augsburg craftsman, and brought up in poverty, passed out of the Technical University in Munich with the most brilliant examination results in the Institution's history. One of his teachers was the founder of modern refrigeration engineering, Carl von Linde, and, from him, Diesel learned a lot of the theory of heat engines. Contemplating this, Diesel saw that he could make an engine four times as efficient as the abysmal steamers of the time, by generating the heat of combustion actually inside the working cylinder, and subjecting the working fluid (air) to as wide a temperature range as possible by utmost compression and expansion. According to his theory, extremely high pressures would be necessary since the temperature reached would partly depend on the pressure—and so the air would have to be compressed before any fuel was introduced, lest combustion be premature.

It was this feature that distinguished the diesel engine from the conventional, spark-ignited, internal-combustion engine that was enjoying contemporaneous development. In the spark-ignition engine, the fuel was mixed with the air before admission to the cylinder, wherein it was compressed as much as was safe before ignition; in the diesel engine, only air was admitted to the cylinder, where it was compressed as much as was necessary to raise it to the temperature at which fuel, then injected into it, would ignite spontaneously.

The first diesel patent was taken out in 1892 in Berlin. His first engine ran on coal dust, but it was when he converted to partially refined oil that it became a success. Unfortunately, Diesel had no business talent, although he might ultimately have profited greatly from the enormous commercial exploitation of his type of engine. He died in 1913 in the North Sea after falling from a ship in which he was travelling for consultations with the British Admiralty. Today, half the world's registered tonnage of ships, a large proportion of its railway locomotives and most commercial vehicles, are diesel driven. There have been, and are, a number of cars similarly powered, but for a variety of good reasons the practice has never been popular with the majority of manufacturers.

In constant-heavy-duty jobs such as those of the locomotive, the earthmover, or the ship, the diesel makes fair sense. In lorries and 'buses its virtues are debatable. In cars they are scarcely detectable. The essentially heavyweight diesel engine is also essentially

Above: compression and combustion in the diesel cycle. Note the glow plug which assists the ignition process when the engine is cold. In the first stages of compression (*left*), the air takes up a swirling motion, forming a vortex. This is brought about partially by the shape of the inlet tract, partially by the piston-crown shape and partially by the combustion-chamber design. As compression progresses, the vortex is broken up into smaller turbulent areas (*centre*). As the fuel is injected, it mixes with the air and begins to ignite. The build-up of compression (*right*) speeds up the combustion process, which continues until injection ceases

Left: the first four-cylinder diesel engine, which was announced by Benz in 1923

537

feeble, and with safety regulations forcing cars to get heavier anyway, there is little attraction in the idea of making them even heavier and, at the same time, denying them the power necessary to move their increased weight at a reasonable rate.

A comparison of diesel and petrol engines built for automotive duty in Europe shows that the average diesel weighs about nine pounds per horsepower. To assess a fair average for petrol engines is more difficult, since so many of them are humble little affairs of a litre or so, intended for cheap, light cars and, because of nature's inexorable square/cube law, such engines must be relatively heavy. However, if we confine ourselves to the larger petrol engines that afford a more direct comparison with the diesels already considered, their power-to-weight ratio works out at about three pounds per horsepower.

This difference is largely due to different marketing requirements. Lightness of a spark-ignition engine does not necessarily imply flimsiness and want of durability, but such engines are built for a market where cost must be low and depreciation can be ridiculously high—in which circumstances it does not pay the manufacturer to make his engines particularly durable. Even so, a lot depends on the pattern of usage: on the rare occasions when a petrol-engined car is used virtually continuously and not subjected to many cold starts and short trips, the engine proves to be capable of covering a very high mileage without overhaul. This is typical of the usage of most diesels, which are commercially operated with maximum utilisation very much in mind. Nevertheless, those rare engine manufacturers, who make both kinds of engines to equally high standards, find very little difference in their durabilities: the general superiority of the diesel from this point of view is simply due to the fact that the diesel *has* to be well and robustly made for, if it is not, it will break under the enormous strain.

Mechanically, the massive construction of the diesel engine is more of a liability than an asset. The thick-crowned pistons are very heavy; so are the connecting rods with their generous big-ends and unusually large gudgeon pins and bosses, and these reciprocating parts impose tremendous loads on the bearings. Consider not only these inertia loads, but also the tremendous compression loads of the diesel, which are likewise ultimately transmitted to the crankcase which has in turn to be inordinately robust. Bear in mind too that the components of a diesel engine are subjected to these heavy mechanical stresses all the time. This is simply because there is no throttle in the air intake of the diesel. When a spark-ignition engine is working at less than full load, the intake is partially closed by the throttle valve linked to the accelerator pedal, and this has the effect of reducing the effective compression ratio: a petrol engine with a ten-to-one compression ratio is only working at five-to-one when running at half throttle. By contrast, the diesel is running at its full compression ratio under all circumstances, the output being varied by metering the dosage of fuel injected. The compression ratio varies from about sixteen to one in large engines to over twenty to one in the smaller varieties used in private cars, and the high consequent loads make life hard for pistons, gudgeon pins and crankshaft bearings. Even worse for them is the shockingly rapid rise in pressure in the cylinders when the fuel is injected, spontaneously bursting into flame. The rigours of the diesel cycle are reflected in the stringent specifications required for bearings and lubricating oils in diesel-engine service.

From the same fact of running constantly at maximum compression comes the first of the diesel

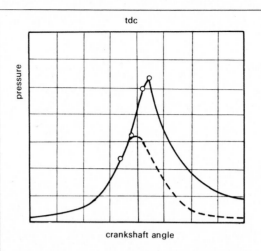

This graph shows the variation of pressure, within a diesel cylinder, as the crankshaft turns and moves the piston up on the compression stroke. The solid curve indicates the situation under normal circumstances (where fuel is injected and combustion takes place), while the dotted line represents the lower pressures found if air alone is compressed. Point 1 is the start of injection; 2 is the start of combustion; 3 is the finish of injection; 4 is the finish of combustion

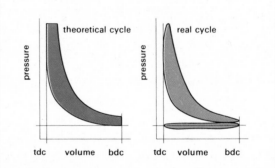

These graphs represent the theoretical and real diesel cycles. The orange area shows the work done on the power stroke, while the blue section is induction and exhaust

engine's advantages, its good part-load fuel economy. Thermal efficiency is intimately related to compression ratio and, in part-load operation, the diesel is greatly superior to the petrol engine. At full load, there is much less difference and what there is may largely be accounted for by the fact that the diesel gives off less waste heat.

The average specific fuel consumption of automotive diesel engines running on full load is about 0.38 lb per horsepower per hour. In the case of petrol engines, the figure is more like 0.48, but this is an average taken from a range that covers wide extremes, and there are plenty of petrol engines that do a good deal better. It is undeniable that the best that petrol engines can do merely equals the average of what diesels manage; but there are in fact not many diesels that get appreciably lower, and the distinguished handful that achieve as little as 0.33 or thereabouts mostly display a somewhat impoverished performance, even by diesel standards.

One of the unfortunate things about the diesel engine is that it has to be run on lean fuel/air mixtures since anything richer would make it smoke intolerably. In the circumstances, it is inevitable that the diesel

The four-stroke diesel cycle is exactly the same as that of the petrol engine (the Otto cycle). However, the pressures within the cylinders are far greater in the case of the diesel unit. Because of these enormous pressures, the engine has to be built very sturdily and is therefore extremely heavy for its size

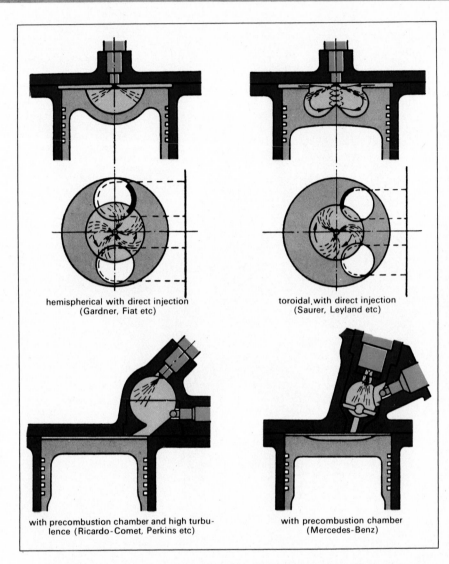

hemispherical with direct injection
(Gardner, Fiat etc)

toroidal with direct injection
(Saurer, Leyland etc)

with precombustion chamber and high turbulence (Ricardo-Comet, Perkins etc)

with precombustion chamber
(Mercedes-Benz)

nature of the fuel is the first consideration: heavy industrial engines can run on all kinds of turgid filth, but automotive diesels require a light petroleum distillate, having about the same calorific content as the petrol used in cars but otherwise exhibiting rather different characteristics. Its anti-knock or octane rating is irrelevant, the corresponding feature being the cetane rating, which is a measure of the fuel's readiness to ignite at a certain temperature and pressure. The two ratings are not related, although a high-cetane fuel will have a low octane value. This is not to say that knock is not a diesel problem: it is, in fact, one of the most notorious, being caused by an exceptionally rapid pressure rise during the course of combustion. Unfortunately, the requirements of good compression/ignition make it impossible to spread the combustion over a longer period, so the entire process of injection of the fuel, volatilisation of the droplets, ignition and combustion, must take place in about thirty degrees of crankshaft rotation. This in turn demands very precise timing of the injection of the fuel, and equally precise metering of the amount injected.

To achieve this, expensive and extremely accurate mechanical pumps jerk the requisite quantities of fuel to spring-loaded nozzles feeding into the combustion chamber. When the pressure at the nozzle is high enough to raise the needle valve off its seat against the spring pressure, it is automatically high enough to ensure that the fuel is sprayed into the combustion chamber in the most minute droplets, and in the most appropriate directions; the amount of fuel delivered is determined by the time during which this pressure can be maintained, governed in turn by the pump in response to the engine speed and the position of the accelerator pedal. The mechanical arrangement of this system is inevitably complex, and these injection components must be viewed as among the most remarkable examples of high-precision, mass-production engineering in the world.

Nevertheless, they suffer severe limitations. As already explained, it is impossible to seek more power from a diesel engine by giving it a richer mixture than normal: excess fuel simply cannot be properly burned, and the residue emerges as grey, or even black, smoke—soot, deriving from the 86 per cent carbon content of the fuel. Smoke is also produced when starting, because the cold engine reduces the temperature of the air compressed in the cylinders and thus impairs the efficiency of combustion. Self-starter motors therefore have to be very powerful to achieve high cranking speeds, and, in fact, the majority of small diesels, such as those used in cars, rely on electrical preheating of the combustion chamber, a procedure that may occupy as much as a minute before starting the engine. Thereafter, no electrical services are required, although in a vehicular application, the engine must be furnished with the usual generator, starter-motor and ancillary equipment. Because of this independence of ignition, the engine cannot be switched off, and is usually stopped by interrupting its fuel supply: the driver pulls a knob which overrides the other injection pump controls and cuts off the fuel.

The smoke given off by a badly adjusted diesel engine is only one of the many pollutants it emits. Its exhaust is also very rich in oxides of nitrogen (on average 1.7 times as much as from the average petrol engine before the introduction of clean air laws), sulphur dioxide (3.8 times as much) and particulate matter, including not only soot but also lead compounds (7.8 times). If the exhaust has an acrid smell, this is caused by aldehydes compounded during

A selection of diesel-engine combustion chambers. Those with precombustion chambers and glow plugs are typical of small, car-size diesels and have higher compression ratios than the others. There are many variations on the toroidal cavity (which is a sort of sphere turned halfway inside-out) and of spray patterns. They all influence the rates of turbulence of the air and of mixture of the fuel therewith. These in turn affect the rates of combustion and pressure-rise

cannot compare with the petrol engine for torque or power. It is worth remembering too that if the diesel is particularly good at fuel economy in part-load operation, this capability is relatively little exploited because the engine has so little power (and the vehicle it propels is so heavy) that it becomes necessary to drive at, or near, full load for a much larger proportion of running time. Precisely the same reasons are responsible for the curve of specific fuel consumption of the diesel being flatter than that of the petrol engine: since the diesel has to run on a relatively weak mixture even at peak bmep (brake mean effective pressure), it is not only less powerful, but also less thirsty. This is the reason, and a poor reason, for relatively low cooling losses at full load.

Likewise, the idea that diesels are strong on torque is a fallacy. Torque curves are usually mirror images of those for specific fuel consumption; and here again, because of the diesel's combustion limitations, the torque curve is particularly flat, giving the illusion of ample torque over a wide range of operating speeds whereas the truth is that the peak of the curve is lopped rather than the lower portions being raised.

The difficulties of burning the charge cleanly and completely, and most of the other limitations of performance of the diesel engine, are attributable to the means by which the fuel is introduced to the air compressed in the cylinder. This makes the processes of injection and combustion matters for serious study, and research on them goes on earnestly and continuously, as it has throughout the history of the type. The

the combustion process which also liberates large quantities of carbon dioxide. On the other hand, the diesel exhaust is notably superior to that of the petrol engine in hydrocarbon and carbon monoxide pollution.

In fairness to the memory of Diesel, it must be pointed out that most of these difficulties would be overcome if current engines retained the fuel injection system that was an important feature of his designs. The way he arranged things, the fuel was heated to the point where it was ready to burn if there were any air in which to do so, and was then forced by compressed air into the combustion chamber, entering as an already burning emulsion. The less satisfactory airless injection system universal today was proposed by a British engineer, Ackroyd-Stuart, who had taken out some oil-engine patents between 1885 and 1890 following-on the work of Priestman of Hull. Another British engineer, McKechnie, vandalised Diesel's design in 1910 by substituting cold airless injection of the fuel for the original and correct hot compressed-air injection.

Another environmentally obnoxious feature of the diesel engine is the noise it makes, a noise that has been found expensive and difficult to cure. If the engine be enclosed by acoustic shielding, most of the noise can be kept from the car's occupants and from outsiders in the vicinity. This is seldom practical because the space for such shielding is seldom available, and if there is room to enclose the engine in a sound-proof box, that box has to be airtight—which means that the normal cooling system will have to be extended and modified in a way that is bound to be costly. Another method, practised to some extent in naval vessels, is to fit a contoured shield of a suitable (and usually heavy) acoustic cladding closely around the engine carcass: in this case, accessibility for maintenance is very difficult, and incorrect fitting of the shield could damage the engine while cooling is still a problem. The long-term solution is to re-design the engine so as to dampen, stiffen or isolate all surfaces that radiate noise. In many cases this is inconsistent with the other mechanical requirements of the components involved, most notably the cylinder block and various timing chests. The noise actually comes from the combustion space, and there is a limit to what can be achieved by modifying it, and the combustion process itself, so as to reduce the noise at source.

Literally, the most burdensome problem of all is the sheer mass of metal necessary to withstand the gross stresses imposed by the ultra-fast pressure rise during combustion. A four-cylinder, 1½-litre diesel engine frequently used in cars develops about 45 bhp and weighs 425 lb; a common 3-litre petrol engine for ordinary saloon cars weighs the same and develops 140 bhp. The same relationship applies to higher power ratings: if 200 bhp were required, it could be obtained from a notably hefty and durable high-grade petrol engine weighing 600 lb, while the equivalent diesel would turn the scale at 1800. The burden of all that extra weight is likely to offset any fuel economies attributable to the diesel. In fact, the penalty is even greater: because the petrol engine is so much smaller and very much faster-revving than a diesel of similar power, most of the transmission line associated with it need only have about one-third the torque capacity of what would be necessary for the compression ignition engine. Only in the final drive, downstream from the reduction gears, need the transmission components be as massive as in diesel-vehicle practice. This means a tremendous saving in weight and an equally tremendous saving in first cost.

As for fuel costs, the differences are largely illusory. At present, diesel fuel is considerably cheaper than

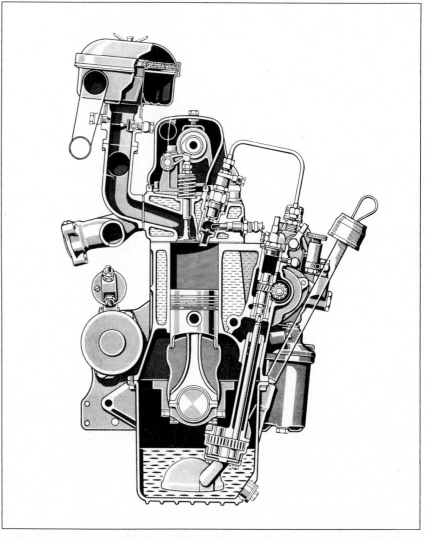

petrol—not at roadside filling stations, but to the big operators who use it in bulk and can buy it a lot more cheaply. Nevertheless, these differences are largely artificial situations brought about by the taxation system, though petrol being the more refined distillate is basically more costly anyway. If there were to be a marked change in the use of these fuels, there would undoubtedly be corresponding changes in the pattern of taxation. In countries where petrol is cheap, very few people bother with diesels, preferring the lower cost and higher efficiency of petrol units.   LJKS

Top: a transverse section through a Mercedes 190D engine of 1958. It is a four-cylinder unit, producing 60 bhp from its 1988 cc

Above: a Scania articulated truck with a turbocharged diesel engine

DISTRIBUTING TORQUE TO THE WHEELS

The differential enables torque to be transmitted to each driving wheel while allowing each one a measure of independence to revolve at different speeds

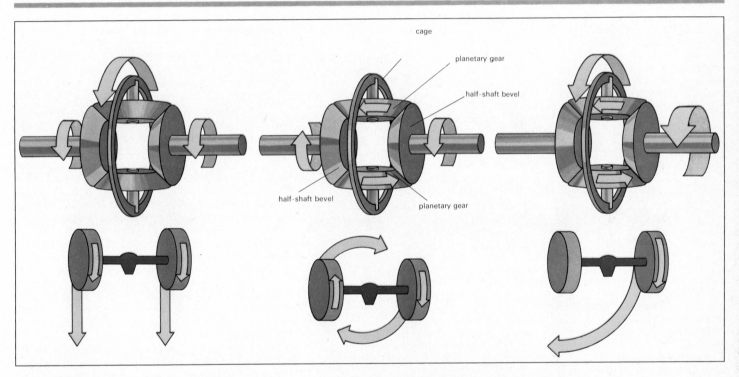

cage

planetary gear

half-shaft bevel

half-shaft bevel

planetary gear

HOUSED WITHIN the final-drive gearing of a car's transmission is a set of gears whose purpose is to allow each driving wheel to receive its share of the torque transmitted from the engine, and yet still enjoy some measure of independence from the other driving wheel, so that the two can revolve at different speeds. It is this set of gears (but not the crown wheel within which they are housed) that is called the differential; and it is needed because when the car is driven round a curve its outer driving wheel must travel a greater distance than the inner one, and therefore complete a greater number of revolutions in the same time. For similar reasons, a car with four-wheel drive needs three differentials: one between the front wheels, one between the rear wheels and another between the front and rear axles.

The important thing to remember about a differential is not that it allows the wheels to rotate at different rates, but that it balances the torque equally between them. At the inner end of each of the half-axle shafts, which drive the wheels, is a bevel gear; these two bevels, facing each other, are linked by two or more mating bevels which are carried in a cage bolted to the final-drive crown-wheel gear. Their path is accordingly an orbit around the axis of the half-shafts, so they are often called star or planetary gears. When the car is being driven in a straight line on a flat road, each tyre will offer the same resistance to engine torque as the other: the loads on the planetary-gear teeth mating with one half-shaft bevel will be the same as those on the teeth mating with the other, so the whole assembly rotates as one. When the car is steered into a curve, the

inner tyre offers more resistance to torque than the outer (because it is being required to do the same amount of work in a shorter distance), and the tooth loads become unequal: the planetary gears then begin to turn, urging the bevel on the outer half-shaft to accelerate until equilibrium is restored.

The mechanism is simple and seldom gives trouble, for the relative speeds of movement of the gear teeth are low, and the operation is only intermittent. However, if the operation should be continuous there could be a danger of overheating: it is therefore important that both driving tyres should have the same effective circumference. Two different brands of tyre that are nominally the same size could easily differ by as much as five per cent in the number of revolutions per mile; the use of a well worn spare tyre on one driving wheel and a new, deep-treaded tyre on the other could produce similar discrepancies (in this context, it is the rolling *circumference*, not *radius*, that matters: in radial-ply tyres especially, the two are not related).

Because the differential balances the torque shared between the two wheels by reacting to differences in the resistance they offer, it cannot allocate to one more than the other is capable of handling. If one tyre should be bogged down in a patch of mud so that it spins freely and cannot develop any grip, it will offer no reactive torque—the tractive torque it can transmit will be nil. Since the torque to each wheel must balance, the other also gets nil: one spins madly, the other stays still and neither does any work; the car does not move.

Faced with such a situation, the skilled driver

Above: diagrammatic representations of the essential working parts of a differential and their relationship to the wheels of a car. In each diagram, the stationary parts are shown in green and the moving ones in blue. Drive is fed to the unit via the cage. If the planetary gears are still (*left*), both half-shafts will rotate at the same speed as the cage. Should the cage be fixed (*centre*), and one wheel turned, the other wheel will turn at an equal speed in the opposite direction. With one wheel held (*right*), the other half-shaft and wheel will turn in the same direction as the cage, but at twice its speed

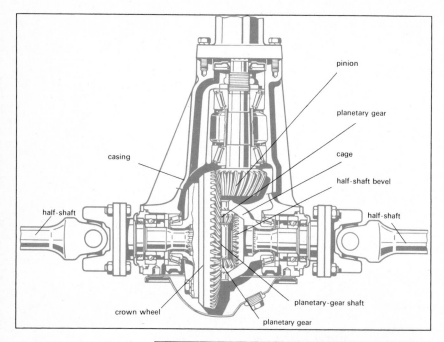

Above: the internal components of a hypoid-bevel final-drive unit, showing the differential components. The set-up shown would be used with either independent or de Dion suspension, since the half-shafts are connected to the unit by universal joints. The casing is filled with oil through the plug shown

Right: a photograph of a differential, showing how the crown wheel is bolted to the cage containing the bevel gears

briefly, in some circumstances, a complete lock) between the differential cage and the half-shafts, by-passing the bevel gears that are within the cage.

The means of achieving this vary somewhat. In the Borg-Warner LSD (limited-slip differential, as commonly abbreviated), cone clutches clamp the half-shaft bevel gears to the inside of the cage; in the Thornton Powr-Lok LSD (made by Dana in the USA, Salisbury in Britain and ZF in Germany, among others), there are plate clutches. Both kinds depend on the very slight movement of the bevels as the planetary gears tend to force them apart in ordinary operation: when runaway wheelspin is incipient, the loss of reaction torque alters this separating force, and the displacement of the gears causes the appropriate clutch to clamp more firmly.

An older type of self-locking differential made by ZF dispenses completely with the gear mechanism inside the cage. Instead, there is a device that resembles a roller bearing gone wrong: the inner and outer tracks or races are not circular, but have a sinusoidal profile, the rollers are not cylindrical but flattened, and the cage carrying them is bolted to the crown wheel. It is, in essence, a sprag clutch or freewheel that is very inefficient: the disparity between power input and output rises sharply with change of relative speed of the half shafts (each of which is connected to one of the annular tracks), so, once again, it is friction that deals with the excess of tractive effort over resistance.

Another gearless LSD, this time from the USA, is the No-Spin. In this, two dog-clutches lock the half-shafts to the flanks of the crown wheel, being lightly spring-loaded into engagement. The angle of the dog faces is such that, if one wheel turns faster than the other, its dogs ride out of engagement. Thus, torque is always transmitted to whichever wheel is offering more resistance and is therefore turning more slowly. The interruption of drive to the faster wheel allows it to slow down and, as soon as the two wheel speeds are rebalanced, the drive to the freed one is again engaged.

It is not because of the need for traction on slippery surfaces that the LSD has become popular for high-powered cars, but because of the need for greater traction and directional stability when accelerating hard or cornering under power. Cars with live rear axles tend to lift their right wheels (because of torque reaction around the final-drive pinion) when accelerating hard, allowing them to spin and impair performance. Cars with a high roll couple tend to lift their inside wheels when cornering hard, again allowing wheel-spin to intrude and severely impair the handling by interrupting the torque to the outer wheel. The LSD is intended to maintain the transmission of torque to the gripping tyre in these conditions.

Racing cars with very wide tyres still need some form of differential locking that can allow free differential action when the amount of grip exceeds the tractive torque available. Cars of really exceptional power, notably the Porsche 917 in its turbocharged Can-Am form, always have enough power to overcome the drag of tyre scrub around corners in the absence of differential action; accordingly, they have no differentials at all. Vintage sports and racing cars with narrow tyres and narrow axle tracks used to be the same, for if their power was much less, their tyre grip was too. The 'solid' axle, with both wheels fixed to the extremities of a single shaft, to which the crown wheel is bolted directly, gives better results when accelerating or lifting a wheel in a corner than any limited-slip or other differential. In ordinary driving, however, it plays havoc with steering response and wears out the tyres at an alarming rate. LJKS

attempts to get out of it by rocking the car backwards and forwards, alternately engaging reverse and forward gears (which is particularly easy with automatic transmission). The secret of this procedure lies in the inertia of the spinning wheel: it is reluctant to change its rate of rotation, let alone its direction, so for a moment, as the clutch is engaged, it will offer some resistance to the torque transmitted to it. For that moment, brief though it may be, the same amount of resistance is translated by the differential into tractive torque for the gripping wheel.

Better still, if the spinning wheel can be held in some way (such as by jamming it with sackcloth or even wedging the parking brake on that side so as to offer some drag), sufficient torque should be available at the other wheel for the car to be moved. This is the principle of the limited-slip differential: by offering some frictional resistance to the runaway spin of the half-shaft driving a tyre bereft of grip, it ensures that some torque may still be delivered to the other. The differential incorporates a locking mechanism that is, in effect, a friction damper making the differential itself more and more inefficient as the disparity between the left and right tyres' reactions grow more and more extreme. These 'diff-lock' contrivances are usually friction clutches which provide a partial lock (or

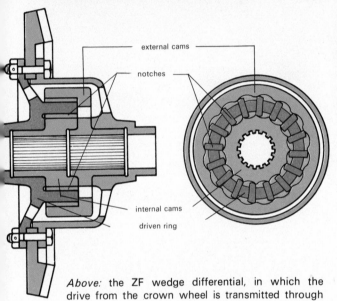

external cams

notches

internal cams

driven ring

Above: the ZF wedge differential, in which the drive from the crown wheel is transmitted through the notched ring to the two axles via the cams; in a straight line the notches engage all cams, but as soon as one wheel speeds up, those cams can slip into the grooves

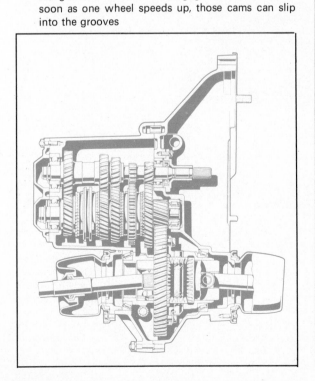

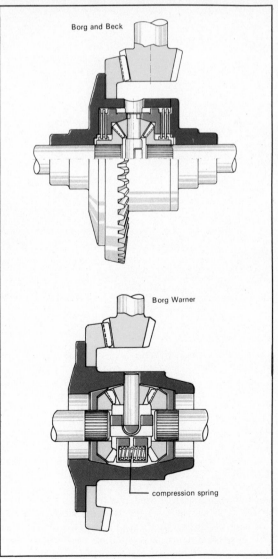

Borg and Beck

Borg Warner

compression spring

Above: an asymmetrical differential cluster, used in instances where the torque has to be split unequally

Above left: a curious double differential used by Desmoulins in their twin-engined car of 1921

Left: two types of limited-slip differential using friction plates; the Borg and Beck relies only on unequal rotation in order to operate, whereas the Borg Warner has a compression spring built in

Far left: the type of differential used on most transverse-engined cars; instead of a crown wheel and pinion, drive is through a pair of helical spur gears

543

PART OF A GERMAN EMPIRE

The history of DKW and Audi are inseparable. From their humble beginnings both developed to play important roles in the giant Audi-NSU-Volkswagen group

Above: pride of the 1974 Audi range, this is the Audi 100 Coupé S. Powered by an 1871 cc, four-cylinder engine, the car has a top speed of 115 mph and produces 112 bhp at 5600 rpm

FOR OVER THREE DECADES, DKW was a leading name in the development of the small, efficient saloon car, pioneering mass production of both front-wheel drive and the two-stroke car engine. Not for nothing did the marque's adherents nickname it 'Das Kleine Wunder' —the little wonder—although the initials really stood for Deutsche Kraftfarzeug Werke.

DKW began life as a motor-cycle manufacturer in the early twenties but, in 1928, it was decided to enter car manufacturing, even though the motor-cycle business was flourishing.

The DKW was built at the Zschopauer Motoren Werke in Berlin at the factory previously occupied by the Deutsche Werke AG, makers of the D-Wagen car. The owner of the DKW factory, Jörgen Rasmussen, decided that he would power his first car with a two-stroke engine of the type which had been so successful in his motor cycles. The engine that he chose was a vertical twin-cylinder unit with dimensions of 68 × 74 mm, giving a capacity of 584 cc and a power output of $16\frac{1}{2}$ bhp. This was relatively modest even for 1928, but Germany was in the midst of a cyclecar boom, occasioned by the onset of the Depression years. Despite the tiny engine, Rasmussen designed quite a sophisticated car around it, for it was fitted into an advanced unitary construction body/chassis largely made from wood. The car had a proven gearbox and even a differential, items which many cyclecar manufacturers deemed unnecessary. The result was that the little DKW became quite popular among the less well off, and many examples of the first DKW car were still in daily use well into the fifties.

DKW did not neglect the sporting market and, for 1930, they introduced a pretty sports car along the same lines. The engine was given different port timing and a higher compression ratio of 5.5 : 1 to raise the power output to 18 bhp. The tiny boat-tailed sports body with separate wings was an instant hit with young drivers and, with an all-up weight of around

10 cwt, it was capable of topping 60 mph—quite a feat for such a small car in 1930. With transverse leaf springs front and rear, it handled as well as most other small sports cars.

The two-stroke DKW engine was beginning to impress many people, for the water-cooled, reverse-scavenged unit was much smoother and easier revving than previous attempts at making two-stroke engines had been, and Rasmussen was encouraged to expand his range upwards. His first effort to this end was to enlarge the engine to 780 cc for the 4/8 saloon of 1930;

in this form, the engine gave 22 bhp, a very good specific output for a small car of this period.

In 1931, the first front-wheel drive DKW appeared. This was the F1, a technically advanced little car which set a high standard for manufacturers of small saloons over the next decade. For the F1, the stroke was reduced from 74 mm to 68 mm to give a capacity of 490 cc and a power output of 15 bhp at 3200 rpm. The twin-cylinder engine was mounted across the frame, and drive was taken to the front wheels via a three-speed gearbox and a multi-plate oil-filled clutch. DKW were to stay faithful to this layout for most of their subsequent models, and it remained virtually

uncopied until Citroën and BMC brought out their transverse-engined, front-wheel-drive cars in the fifties.

The F1 had a ladder-type steel frame with independent front suspension by swing axles, and a dead axle on transverse leaf springs at the rear. The body was now made from steel but, even so, the two-seater F1 weighed little more than 10 cwt and was good for 50 mph. An almost identical car, the F2, was built alongside the F1, the only major difference being the engine size, which was the original 584 cc unit, still giving 18 bhp at 3200 rpm.

Rasmussen's determination to stick with small cars paid off for, in the Depression years, he was able to survive and even expand. In the year 1928, he had become the majority shareholder in Audi, the company started by August Horch, and, in 1932, he gathered into his fold both Horch and Wanderer factories. The four companies in the group, Horch, Audi, Wanderer and DKW—were grouped under one name—Auto Union—and the company badge was designed to show four inter-linked rings. The new company was rivalled in size and prestige only by the Mercedes-Benz group.

Rasmussen was presented with a bewildering

Far left, top to bottom
The first DKW of them all, the 584 cc, two-stroke-engined machine of 1928

In 1930, DKW produced the P25 range offered in several versions, this being the saloon model

The DKW Sonderklasse 32PS of 1938/9 featured a four-cylinder 1050 cc engine driving the front wheels

Above: the neatly made F1 model of 1931 powered by a tiny 490 cc, twin-cylinder, two-stroke engine mounted across the frame

Above left: the F1 model was later developed to become the Meisterklasse. This range retained the vertical-twin-cylinder, two-stroke layout, but the motor was enlarged to 684 cc

selection of cars, ranging from his own tiny DKWs, through the medium sized Wanderer range, to the larger Audi and even bigger 5-litre straight 8 Horch.

The DKW and Horch cars were allowed to continue on their own lines, but both Wanderer and Audi were intermingled to a large extent over the ensuing years and, by the outbreak of World War II, both makes were being produced only in small numbers. Wanderer began car production in 1911 with a small, two-seater, 1150 cc car, popularly known as the Püppchen (doll), and from then on they made workmanlike but unexceptional cars until the merger in 1932. They had, however, built most of their engines with overhead valves at a time when the side valve was almost universal on cheaper cars.

Audi had a rather more distinguished history, largely because they tended to build bigger, more sporting cars. After being forced to sell his own company in 1906, due largely to his preoccupation with engineering at the expense of finance, August Horch started up again in 1909 just down the road

from his old factory in Zwickau. He called the firm Audi, which is the Latin for Horch. His first car under the new name was the B10/28, powered by a 2.6-litre engine; this was followed by the C14/35 'Alpensieger', with a four-cylinder, 3.5-litre engine giving 35 bhp at 1700 rpm. The standard model was capable of 55 mph, but Horch, who was fond of taking part in the strenuous Alpine Trial, built a lightweight car with a much shorter wheelbase than the 10 ft of the standard tourer, and fitted it with an aluminium body. This car was particularly successful, winning the Alpine Trials of 1912, 1913 and 1914, hence the name of Alpensieger —Alpine winner. The company also catalogued two larger engined cars in the years leading up to the war; one, the D18/45 had a 4.6-litre engine and the other, the E22/50, had a 5.6-litre unit.

After World War 1, the pre-war range was again put into production but a new car, the model K, was soon announced. This had a 3½-litre, four-cylinder engine mounted in unit, not only with the gearbox, but with the radiator and steering box as well. The engine gave about 50 bhp and moved the car along at 60 mph.

The K was the forerunner of perhaps the best Audi built up to that time; this was the M18/70 which first appeared in 1923. It was powered by a 4.6-litre, overhead-camshaft, six-cylinder engine which had a block cast in silicon aluminium, duralumin connecting rods, steel cylinder-liners and a seven-bearing crankshaft. It was a smooth unit which gave 70 bhp at a modest 3000 rpm and was capable of shifting the big car along at 75 mph. It was able to hold its own with many of the best German cars of the time and was in steady demand despite its high price.

However, the fortunes of Audi began to decline gradually. Horch himself, although still a board member, no longer had anything to do with design; and the firm went deeper into trouble when they introduced an 8-cylinder car in 1928. This car, the R type or Imperator, had a straight-eight, 4.8-litre engine giving 100 bhp. It made use of several light metals but was a prosaic side-valve unit. Even the chassis layout was ordinary, with leaf springs on the rigid axles front and rear, although the rear axle case was made from silicon aluminium. It was a big, heavy

Opposite page, far left top to bottom
1951 DKW F89 Meisterklasse

1953 896 cc Sonderklasse

DKW-Auto Union 1000 coupé

Opposite page, near left, above and below
1911 Audi B10/28 hp

1913 Audi sports

This page, top to bottom
1923 Audi K14/50HP

1930 six-cylinder Audi Dresden

1937 Audi 225

1939 two-seater sports version of the Audi 225

chassis on which some attractive bodies were fitted and, although it was capable of cruising at 75 mph, there was a declining demand for prestige cars.

Rasmussen made an offer for Audi in 1928, which the directors accepted, and he became the controlling shareholder. His first aim was to build cheaper cars, so he reached agreement with the American Rickenbacker company to build their engines under licence. Six- and eight-cylinder engines were built by Audi, but the Rickenbacker engines were rather dull side-valve 3.8 and 5-litre engines which had neither great power nor sophistication. These units were fitted to the Zwickau and Dresden models while the Imperator carried on in production until 1932, the year of the merger.

Audi's individuality gradually disappeared after the merger until the factory was really an assembly area for parts supplied by others in the group; in fact, the firm was obliged to move to the Horch works so there was little left of the old Audi company after 1932. Rasmussen introduced a cheaper Audi in 1931, using a Peugeot 4-cylinder 1100 cc engine in a DKW chassis. This never got into full production so, in 1932, Audi introduced a new model, the 225, which featured an enlarged DKW front-wheel-drive chassis into which had been fitted a Wanderer 2.3-litre six-cylinder engine, the chassis being clothed in a body designed at the Horch factory. The engine was interesting as it had been designed before the merger by Ferdinand Porsche; it was a light ohv six using an alloy block, cast-iron cylinder head, wet liners and a seven-bearing crankshaft. Wanderer never developed the engine to give very much power, and it had only a relatively feeble 40 bhp at 3500 rpm. The car suffered various teething troubles connected with the gearbox and steering, and it never sold in any quantity.

DKW remained the best selling car in the Auto Union group during the thirties largely because the company remained faithful to small cars. The F1 model was developed into the Reichsklasse, with a 584 cc engine, and the Meisterklasse of 684 cc, still retaining the vertical-twin, two-stroke layout and front-wheel drive. The cars had become larger, with a wheelbase of over 8 ft but this allowed the use of a full four-seater body, which had returned to the wood and fabric construction of the early models. DKW also produced a range of conventional cars alongside the front-wheel-drive models. These cars, known as the Sonderklasse and Schwebeklasse, used a V4 engine at the front, driving the rear axle, but the inherent roughness of the V4 coupled with the relatively modest power output of 26 bhp from the 1054 cc engine caused sales to proceed at a dribble compared with the booming sales of the front-wheel-drive cars. Exports of the small cars built up well in the thirties and, in England, they established a small but expanding foothold in the market.

Auto Union became heavily involved in motor racing in the early thirties with the V16 car, but most of the work was carried out at the Horch factory to Porsche designs and, as the Nazi Government was subsidising the racing programme, it had little effect on the production programme, neither influencing design nor affecting adversely the company's financial situation.

The twin-cylinder DKWs continued in production right up to the outbreak of war in 1939, differing only in minor details apart from the increasing sumptuousness of the bodies which were becoming heavier all the time. As well as four-door saloons there was a handsome cabriolet with wire wheels.

In 1938, Audi, who had persevered with the dull Rickenbacker-engined cars, introduced the 920, a much more ambitious car. Using a box-section chassis with independent front suspension by wishbones and transverse-leaf springs, and a rigid rear axle with transverse-leaf springs, the car was powered by a six-cylinder engine which was evolved simply by removing two cylinders from the Horch straight-8. With dimensions of 87×92 mm and a capacity of 3281 cc, this single-overhead-camshaft engine produced 82 bhp at 3600 rpm which was good enough to propel the big saloon and cabriolet bodies at 85 mph with ease. Having a good synchromesh four-speed gearbox with overdrive, and sumptuous bodies, Audi were once again in a position to challenge the prestige cars of Germany, but production was sadly curtailed by the onset of war.

From 1939 to 1944, the Auto Union factories settled down to war production, largely aeroplane engines and parts, but DKW did continue car production until 1941; they even had a brand new three-cylinder, two-stroke-engined car ready for production in 1940 but it was abandoned.

At the end of the war, the Auto Union factories were occupied by the Russians, and later the East German authorities nationalised them. Car production gradually started up again but, as the Auto Union company had the rights to use the names Horch, Audi, DKW and Wanderer, the East Germans called their DKW derivative the Trabant, while the new 'Horch' was

Above: in 1965, the Audi name was revived and given to a range of attractive and reliable saloon cars. This is the 1971 Audi 100GL which used the four-cylinder 1871 cc engine driving the front wheels

Right: a feature of the Audi 80 model is this ingenious self-stabilising steering system which prevents swerving to one side due to a flat tyre. This characteristic is the result of an unconventional steering geometry layout. The imaginary extension of the steering-pivot inclination axis (pivot point around which the wheel swivels) meets the road surface outboard of a vertical line running through the centre of the wheel rim. This is known as the negative steering roll radius

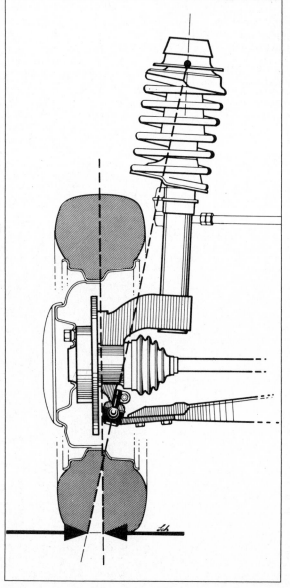

known as the Sachsenring. In Poland, a copy of the pre-war two-cylinder DKW was known as the Syrena, while an East German company, Wartburg, also built cars to DKW designs. The names of Horch and Wanderer died at the outbreak of the war but a new Auto Union company was formed in 1949 to produce the DKW again. The factory was situated in Dusseldorf, and initial production was centred on an updated version of the Meisterklasse, with a two-cylinder engine and a modern body. Once the factory was established and had begun supplying car-starved Europe, they resurrected the 3-cylinder design of 1940. This engine, with bore and stroke of 71×76 mm had a capacity of 896 cc and developed 34 bhp at 4000 rpm on a compression ratio of 6.5:1. It was mated to a four-speed gearbox with synchromesh on the top three; top speed for the standard saloon was in the region of 75 mph. Suspension followed pre-war practice, with wishbones and transverse-leaf springs at the front and a dead axle with transverse leaf springs at the rear. This new Sonderklasse model caught on well with the public, and it was soon being produced as both a two and four-seater drop-head coupé and a station wagon, as well as the normal four-seater saloon.

A new model with the engine increased in size to 981 cc and a power output of 40 bhp was marketed under the Auto Union name and was known as the Auto Union 1000. The more sporting versions were also known as Auto Unions, largely to cash-in on the marque's pre-war reputation. The most popular models were the 100 SP Coupé and Convertible which had attractive modern bodies; both cars were capable of exceeding 90 mph and they established a keen following of discerning buyers over the years.

The bulbous-bodied Sonderklasse was superseded by the Junior, which had a more modern body as well as torsion bar front and rear suspension. This two-door saloon was good for 75 mph and had the option of the Saxomat automatic clutch.

The Junior was followed by the F11, F12 and F102 saloons, each having improvements over the earlier models mainly in the interior accommodation and styling, but all the cars retained the basic mechanical components of the Sonderklasse.

In 1956, Mercedes-Benz had gained a majority shareholding in Auto Union, but they made no great attempt to interfere with the design of the cars, leaving the company to go its own way.

The competition potential of the two-stroke DKW engine was realised in the late fifties when a Heidelberg engineer, Fritz Wenk, built a glassfibre-bodied car called the Monza which used a tuned engine in a near-standard DKW chassis. This sold quite well in Germany and won a few competition events as well as taking a number of class speed records at the Monza track in Italy, from where it gained its name.

The German tuners, Dieter Mantzel and Gerhard Mitter, began to extract phenomenal power outputs from the DKW 'three', and they started to win hill-climbs and other short distance events, but the engines tended to overheat when held at peak-revs in circuit races. Mitter designed a sports version of the engine using four upright cylinders for which he claimed 130 bhp, but it seldom held together for very long. He also used a three-cylinder engine in Formula Junior racing as did Britain's Elva but, although the engine showed promise, the centre piston always overheated.

By the early sixties, enthusiasm for the two-stroke was beginning to wane despite the success of Saab, who had used a two-stroke engine similar to the DKW with great success in competition. Sales gradually began to decline in the face of the more sophisticated four-stroke engines now on the market. Volkswagen had taken away the company's volume sales and, in 1964, Volkswagen acquired a controlling interest. Sales of the two-stroke cars continued into 1966 and, in 1965, the name of Audi was resurrected for a new front-wheel-drive car, the Audi 80. This used the body and most of the suspension components of the DKW F102, but the two-stroke engine was replaced by a 1.7-litre four-cylinder unit giving 80 bhp at 5000 rpm. The car was immediately successful and subsequent models such as the extremely stylish 90 and 100 series have been equally popular.

Volkswagen took control of the NSU factory and merged it with Audi, and the company began producing some advanced ideas from their engineering department. The Wankel-engined NSU Ro80 was one result, while, in 1972, Volkswagen were obliged to use a front-wheel drive Audi design, the new 80 model, to bolster the Volkswagen empire, due to flagging sales of the Beetle. The Audi 80 is also sold under the VW name as the Passat.

Although it seems unlikely that the DKW name will ever again be used on a car, some of the principles laid down by Rasmussen many years ago, are still being adhered to in the Audi range. No one could ask for a better epitaph than that.   MT

Below: The Audi 80 range was introduced in 1972 to compete in the 1½-litre, four-seater family-saloon market. It is produced in two engine sizes, 1296 cc or 1471 cc, and a choice of two- or four-door models is also available

HELL RAISERS FROM MICHIGAN

John and Horace Dodge liked nothing more than a stiff drink and a good fight. Yet, they were astute businessmen

THE SUPERINTENDENT OF THE engineering works at Windsor, Ontario glowered at the two young workmen. 'We've come for the job,' said the elder and more domineering of the two.

'We need only one man,' said the superintendent.

The retort was swift. 'We're brothers and we always work together. If you haven't room for two of us, then neither will start. That's that!' The Dodge brothers, John Francis and Horace Elsin, were like that. Though there was four years' difference in their ages—John was born in 1864, Horace in 1868—they were as inseparable as if they were twins. Both were red-

Above: the first Dodge built was this four-seater tourer, powered by a four-cylinder, 3½-litre engine

Right, top to bottom
1918 Dodge coupé

John and Horace Dodge pictured in Detroit in 1914

1918 Dodge hardtop

headed and both were quick tempered. They were, it was said, always ready to quarrel with anybody else or each other.

John was the natural leader, pushy and talkative; Horace was usually quiet, tolerant and slow-moving. They had left their birthplace, Niles, Michigan, in the early 1880s, determined to become engineers. They found work, and gained valuable experience, in machine shops in Detroit and Windsor; their idea of relaxation, once the week's work was over, was to spend Saturday night in a favourite saloon in the roughest part of downtown Detroit drinking themselves to a standstill.

One night, John ordered the bar owner to climb on to a table and dance. When the man refused, John pulled out a revolver and repeated his request. This time the man obeyed, while John hurled glasses at the mirror behind the bar. However, once he had sobered up, he happily paid for the damage.

In 1899, the brothers organised the Evans and

Dodge Bicycle Company in Windsor to produce a four-point-bearing bicycle of their own invention. When a Canadian group made a successful takeover bid, the brothers moved back to Detroit, where they established one of the best machine shops in the Middle West. Order, cleanliness and efficiency were its hallmarks and soon they were making components for the infant motor industry.

When, in February 1903, Henry Ford asked them to produce the chassis for his new venture, the Ford Motor Company, the Dodges were already considering substantial offers from the Oldsmobile and Great Northern companies, but there seemed to be far greater profits to be made from the new company so, on 28 February, the two brothers signed a formal agreement with Henry Ford to provide 650 chassis for Ford's first season of production.

The brothers undertook to deliver the chassis to Ford's assembly plant on Mack Avenue, Detroit, at a cost of $250 each—a total of $162,500. In return, they would receive the first payment of $5000 on 15 March, provided that they could show that they had invested that sum in equipment to service the Ford contract. If the investment was then doubled, they would get the next $5000 a month later, plus another $5000 when the first batch of chassis was delivered. This $15,000 was to pay for the first sixty engines delivered, the next forty would be paid for in cash as they were completed, and thereafter there would be a regular payment every fortnight.

It was an arrangement that suited both parties; the Dodges might not have had much formal education, but they were shrewd businessmen, and had known Ford for several years.

Within a short while, the Dodge works were engaged virtually one hundred per cent on building Ford chassis, employing a staff of 150. Deliveries started in early July, and soon Ford was assembling fifteen complete Model A cars a day. The Dodges employed their staff on piecework rates, which resulted in some slipshod workmanship, but, as the brothers had invested $10,000 in the Ford company, and as John had been made a director, they soon rectified this state of affairs, and sales forged ahead.

When Ford introduced the Model N in November 1905, it was announced that the mechanism for the new car would be made entirely within the new Ford factory on Piquette Avenue and that the Dodge brothers would make the chassis for the larger Ford cars only.

The brothers were now given 350 shares each in the Ford Motor Company, and John became Vice-President. However, as time went on, the independent Dodges became more and more dissatisfied with the prices they were receiving for the transmissions, rear axles, drive shafts and forgings that they were supplying to Ford. They were worried, too, that Ford might suddenly cancel their contract and leave them high and dry. By 1912, they were determined on a course of action: they would become independent of Ford, and build their own cars. In August 1913, John Dodge resigned from the board of the Ford Motor Company, though he maintained friendly relations with Henry Ford, and the brothers continued as shareholders. In fact, the 2000 shares that the brothers now held provided a large proportion of the backing for the new venture. They were receiving over a million dollars a year in dividends, and their properties were estimated to be worth $30–$40 million.

The Dodge car was unveiled on 14 October 1914; it was produced in the new Dodge factory at Hamtramck, Detroit, which had been built on a site acquired in 1910. The car was a conventionally designed four-cylinder model of $3\frac{1}{2}$ litres capacity, with a power output of 25 bhp. There were two distinctive features: the gear-change operated 'back-to-front', and the 12-volt electrical system incorporated a North-East dynastarter unit which automatically restarted the engine, should it stall with the ignition switched on.

Thanks to the company's long association with Ford, the Dodge name was already well-known throughout the American auto trade, and soon more than 22,000 dealers across the States were clamouring for agencies for the new car.

Below
1924 15 cwt Dodge van

1930 Eight DC

1936 D2 coupé

Right: the Dodge Coronet D30 of 1949

Above: enough to turn anyone's head, the elaborately styled V8 Dodge of 1963

Right, top to bottom: The 1961 Dodge Polara model. Note the pillarless side-windows which were so popular during the early 1960s.

The 1963 version of the Polara showing the more sombre lines of the later model

Another styling feature that became popular with American motorists was the 'fastback', shown here to perfection on the 1966 Dodge Charger

The marque's rise was meteoric: by 1916, annual production was America's fourth biggest, with over 70,000 cars delivered. A big boost to Dodge sales came that year when General 'Black Jack' Pershing ordered 250 Dodge staff cars to help him in his campaign against the Mexican bandit, Pancho Villa. Villa subsequently returned the compliment by adopting the Dodge as his official car—but he was killed while riding in it in 1923.

John and Horace Dodge may have been illiterate, but they coined a word to describe the Dodge's performance that became an everyday term: dependability. In 1920, the Dependable Dodge was second only to the Model T in sales. By this time, the link with Ford had been finally severed: alarmed by Henry Ford's insistence, in 1916, that he would henceforth ignore dividends altogether, except for purely nominal payments, the Dodges brought a suit to protect their income. It ended in Ford buying them out—and all the other shareholders in the Ford Motor Company—for a total of $106 million, of which the Dodge Brothers' share was $25 million. However, although the case was hard fought, personal relationships between the Dodges and Henry Ford remained friendly and free of bitterness.

A major breakthrough came in 1916, when Budd all-steel tourer coachwork was adopted as a standard feature (a few all-steel saloons were also built). However, this was not the first time that this construction had been used on a production vehicle, for BSA and Stoneleigh in Britain had featured all-steel coachwork as early as 1911.

In life, John and Horace Dodge had been inseparable; in death, too, they were not parted, for in 1920 they died of pneumonia within a few months of each other. Ownership of the company passed to their widows, with Frederick J. Haynes, formerly Vice-President and General Manager, taking over the management of the firm, which was now making 1000 cars a day.

This situation continued until 1925, when the New York bankers Dillon, Read & Company took over Dodge for a reputed $146 million, of which $50 million represented goodwill, written down in the Dodge accounts as being worth $1!

The company's sole product was still the original $3\frac{1}{2}$-litre four (now available either as a car or as a truck), although the basic design had been steadily

Left: the two-door Dodge Dart of 1960 featured heavy bumpers, tail-fins, pillarless side windows and a 4½-litre engine

Below: 1959 saw the tail-fin craze reach its climax. Typical of this styling trend was the Dodge Custom Royal of that year. This model also featured enormous tail lights and heavy chrome-plated bumpers

Opposite page, top right: a 1970 Dodge Charger convertible. Various engine options were offered, ranging in power from 330 to 425 bhp

Opposite page, bottom right: the car which became a cult symbol in America, the Dodge Charger RT. It featured a V8, 430 bhp engine

Below: the 1974 Dodge Charger SE. Although still powered by the V8 engine, the car has become more refined than earlier models with the same name

refined over the years. The 1923 models, for example, had pioneered the stop lamp and the anti-theft lock—fitted, in this instance, on the gearbox, but four-wheel-brakes seem never to have been available on the Dodges imported into England, and were apparently only fitted for the last few months of the model's life in America during 1928. Although the company boasted of its 'sound financial standing, which permits uninterrupted development and adherence to the policy of constant improvement', its unadventurous marketing policy had brought it to the brink of financial disaster by 1927. Clarence Dillon of Dillon, Read & Company approached Walter Chrysler—and found him receptive to buying Dodge. After days of haggling, the two agreed on terms: Chrysler was to acquire Dodge for $70 million in stock plus the interest payments on Dodge bonds, worth $56 million. The merger, sneered one financier, was 'like a minnow swallowing a whale', but Chrysler always claimed: 'The greatest thing I ever did was to buy Dodge'.

He had acquired one of the world's largest and best-organised motor factories: the Hamtramck plant now covered 58 acres and employed 2000 people. It was a move essential to his continued expansion. Minutes after the contract giving Chrysler control was signed, his Chief Production Manager, Kaufmann T. Keller, had huge canvas signs reading 'Chrysler Corporation, Dodge Division' hung over the entrance gates, then marched in to take control—on 30 July 1928.

A new six-cylinder model, the Senior Six, had been introduced in 1927; its specification included four-wheel-hydraulic brakes and a seven-bearing crankshaft with pressure lubrication, and it was to this model that Walter Chrysler looked for the company's future expansion. The old-four-cylinder model was rapidly pensioned off, and replaced by a new cheap six, the Victory, fitted with a short-stroke version of the Senior's power unit; in 1930, an even smaller six, the 19.8 hp 2.6-litre, appeared. At the extremely reasonable price in Britain of £297 for a saloon, it represented remarkable value for money.

At the same time, Dodge brought out a 26.4 hp straight-eight, with a power unit similar to that of the contemporary Chrysler; this model was only cata-

Right: the 1974 Dodge Dart Sport. By 1974, the styling of American cars had become much more sophisticated with smooth flowing lines. The Dart is the smallest of the current Dodge models excluding, of course, the Japanese Mitsubishi Colt, now marketed in America as the Dodge Colt

Far right: top of the 1974 model range is the Monaco Brougham powered by a bewildering variety of engine options

Bottom far right: the Monaco Brougham is available not only with a host of engine options, but with a number of body styles, including two-door and four-door versions, and a station wagon model. The station wagon, too, is available in several different versions including six and nine-passenger models

logued until 1933. By that time, the Victory and Senior Six had acquired styling similar to that of the Model B Ford. These cars, claimed the Dodge copywriters, had 'every modern feature, not merely one'. The specification included automatic clutch; easy-change, silent gearbox; freewheeling; hydraulic brakes; non-burning, non-pitting valve seat inserts; self-oiling springs; Airwheel tyres; double drop X-type frame and a welded, monopiece steel body.

The virtues of the coachwork seemed a little ominous, however: the company said 'A Dodge steel body may be dented, it cannot be shattered—nor is there any wood to feed a sudden flame'.

Nevertheless, Dodge was once again the industry's fourth biggest manufacturer, with sales of 86,000 in 1933. Despite their close links with Chrysler, Dodge never adopted the controversial Airflow styling entirely, although their 1935 models followed the more orthodox vee-bonneted Airstream look.

For 1936, the Senior Six acquired, as standard, the new Chrysler automatic overdrive transmission, in which a centrifugal clutch brought in the overdrive top-gear when the car was cruising at speeds over 45 mph; rationalisation had by now proceeded to the

point where the Dodge had precious little of its former individuality remaining, and few changes other than new body styling and independent front suspension were made during the remainder of the period just prior to World War II.

There was little to choose between the Chrysler Corporation marques in post-war days, either; indeed, some Plymouth models were sold as Dodges in export markets, and all shared a common bodyshell, introduced in 1949. The faithful old L-head six was still the Dodge's power unit, although in 1953 the option of the new Red Ram V8 was offered—and taken up by more than half the customers. What had been a relatively simple model range suddenly became highly complex: the 1954 line-up comprised eight basic series, two wheelbase lengths and two power units, all mixed according to choice.

Chrysler Corporation cars were dramatically restyled in 1955, although the same power-unit options continued. Larger engines and push-button automatic transmission made their appearance on the 1956 line, and a new four-door hardtop, the Lancer, made its debut. Powered normally by one of Dodge's V8 power plants, it could also be ordered with the side-

valve six. Another new model was the Custom Sierra Station Wagon, which could be purchased with either two or three rows of seats; in the latter form, it seated eight passengers.

Ride comfort was improved on 1957 models by the introduction of 'Torsion-Aire' torsion-bar front suspension plus oversize 14-inch tyres. The range now consisted of the Coronet, Royal, Suburban, Sierra and Kingsway, mostly with the Red Ram V8, although two six-cylinder models were still listed.

In 1958, the Chrysler Corporation produced its 25-millionth vehicle and, that year, Dodge cars underwent a fairly comprehensive facelift, gaining wrap-around, compound-curved windscreens and quadruple headlights in a restyled grille. Under the bonnet, a major innovation was the option of an electronically controlled fuel-injection system, which boosted the Red Ram's power output to 333 bhp. More than seventy per cent of the sales that year were of the Dodge Coronet range, and an astonishing 96.4 per cent of all cars produced were fitted with automatic transmission. Indicative of the driving priorities of the average American family motorist were two other statistics: 62.5 per cent of the cars produced had power-assisted steering, yet only 34 per cent could boast power braking.

By now, the side-valve six was definitely on the way out: only one 1959 model offered it, and that was the rock-bottom of the range, the Coronet MD1-L. Within a year, it disappeared completely.

Styling was at its nadir in 1959: tailfins had been growing in size throughout the decade and now, under the name of 'Swept-Wing Styling', they became positively overpowering. Twin radio aerials and juke-box-style rear lights completed the aesthetic mess. Top of the range was the Custom Royal four-door hardtop, which was available with 305, 320 or 345 bhp V8 power units, while the Sierra station wagon catered for the 'Quiverfulls' by offering six or nine-passenger versions also available with various engine options.

In 1961, the Lancer name was revived for a new compact, this time based on the Plymouth Valiant, but the company's general trend during the 1960s was to build bigger. Its late-1960s 'compact', the Dart, boasted a $4\frac{1}{2}$-litre engine. This model was backed up by the larger Coronets with six or eight-cylinder engines with overhead valves, plus the 6.3-litre Polara and 7.2-litre Monaco.

Mindful that it was missing out on the sub-compact market, the company concluded a deal in 1971 to import the Mitsubishi Colt sub-compact from Japan. This model became steadily more Dodge and less Japanese, until a complete restyling, in 1974, brought the options of 1.6 or 2-litre engines and Chrysler-built Torquelite automatic transmission. The 2-litre package incorporated the automatic transmission and vacuum-servo disc brakes as standard. Hydraulic-type safety bumpers were fitted to saloon and estate versions, while the coupé and hardtop variants merely used larger over-riders. Safety features included seat belts that had to be fastened before the ignition could be switched on. Fuel consumption was 18 to 22 miles per US gallon.

However, the Colt was only a partial solution to the company's problems resulting from the fuel crisis, for the Chrysler Corporation had just committed itself to a programme of new large cars, which were a drug on the market as soon as they were introduced.

The question to be asked was how long could Dodge rely on the Colt for its sub-compact sales? Would it be the old story of waking up to market trends far too late to profit from them?   DBW

DODGE CHARGER

The Dodge Charger is available in two body styles, a two-door hardtop and a two-door coupé; there is very little to distinguish them except for rear quarter windows in the hardtop. There is, as is usual with a popular American series, a vast number of variations to running gear. There are six different engines —a 105 bhp six-cylinder unit, and five V8s of 150, 175, 240, 260 and 280 bhp respectively.

A three-speed manual gearbox is standard on the six-cylinder and 150 bhp models, while a three-speed Torqueflite automatic transmission is standard on the 175 and 280 bhp V8s. The automatic is optional on the 'six' and on the 150, which also has the option of the four-speed manual gearbox, and on the 240 and 260s.

Suspension on all models is independent at the front by means of wishbones, lower-trailing links, longitudinal torsion bars and telescopic dampers, and non-independent at the rear, with a rigid axle, semi-elliptic leafsprings and tele-scopic dampers. A front anti-roll bar is available on the Charger SE, which is a sports version of the standard car.

Braking is by means of discs at the front and drums at the rear. Cars with engines producing over 150 bhp have servo assistance as standard.

An interesting feature on all the Charger models is that they have electronic ignition systems.

The Charger's sleek two-door, five/six-seater body is rounded off nicely by spoke-type wheels.

ENGINE Front-mounted, water-cooled straight-six or V8. 86.4 mm (3.40 in) bore × 104.6 mm (4.12 in) stroke = 3687 cc (225 cu in) (105 straight-six); 99.2 mm (3.91 in) bore × 84 mm (3.31 in) stroke = 5211 cc (318 cu in) (150 V8); 102.5 mm (4.04 in) bore × 84 mm (3.31 in) stroke = 5572 cc (340 cu in) (240 V8); 110.2 mm (4.34 in) bore × 85.8 mm (3.38 in) stroke = 6555 cc (400 cu in) (175 and 260 V8s); or 109.7 mm (4.32 in) bore × 95.2 mm (3.75 in) stroke = 7210 cc (440 cu in) (280 V8); maximum power (DIN) between 105 and 280 bhp; maximum torque (DIN) 185 lb ft (105), 265 lb ft (150), 305 lb ft (175), 295 lb ft (240), 335 lb ft (260) or 380 lb ft (280). Cast-iron block and heads; compression ratio 8.2:1 (175, 260 and 280),

8.4:1 (105), 8.5:1 (240) or 8.6:1 (150); 4 main bearings (straight-six) or 5 main bearings (V8s). 2 valves per cylinder operated by a single camshaft— side (straight-six), or at centre of V (V8). 1 Holley down-draught, single-barrel carburettor (105), 1 Carter downdraught twin-barrel carburettor (150), 1 Holley downdraught twin-barrel carburettor (175), or 1 Carter downdraught 4-barrel carburettor (240, 260 and 280).

TRANSMISSION Single-dry-plate clutch or torque converter. 3 or 4-speed manual transmission or 3-speed Torqueflite automatic. 3-speed manual ratios: 1st 3.08, 2nd 1.7, 3rd 1, reverse 2.900:1; final-drive ratio 3.21:1 (3.23 and 3.55 optional). 4-speed manual ratios: 1st 2.47, 2nd 1.77, 3rd 1.34, 4th 1, reverse 2.22:1; final-drive ratio 3.23:1. 3-speed automatic ratios: 1st 2.45, 2nd 1.45, 3rd 1, reverse 2.2:1; final-drive ratio 3.230:1. Rear wheels driven.

CHASSIS Integral.

SUSPENSION Front—independent by means of wishbones, lower-trailing links, longitudinal torsion bars and telescopic dam-

pers (anti-roll bar optional, standard on Charger SE); rear—non independent by a live axle, semi-elliptic leaf springs and tele-scopic dampers.

STEERING Recirculating ball; 5.3 turns from lock to lock; power-assistance optional.

BRAKES Discs front and drums rear. Servo assistance on all models over 150 bhp.

WHEELS 5 or 6 inch × 14.

TYRES E78 × 14.

DIMENSIONS AND WEIGHT Wheelbase 115 in; track 61.9 in front, 62 in rear; length 212.7 in; width 77 in; height 52.2 in; ground clearance 5.40 in; kerb weight 3570 lb coupé or 3950 lb hardtop; turning circle between walls 41.20 ft; fuel tank 21 gallons.

PERFORMANCE Maximum speed 98 mph (105), 108 mph (150), 110 mph (175), 115 mph (240), 117 mph (260) or 119 mph (280); fuel consumption 17.8 mpg (105), 16.3 mpg (150), 15.3 mpg (175), 14.8 mpg (240), 14.6 mpg (260) or 12.5 mpg (280).

THE FULFILMENT OF A TEAM MANAGER'S DREAM

Not for nothing do American racing fans call Mark Donohue 'Captain Nice'. He is
well mannered, articulate, versatile, a gifted engineer and a brilliant driver

MARK DONOHUE, WHO RETIRED from motor racing at the end of the 1973 racing season, was one of the most distinguished of the United States' large number of racing drivers who began to invade the world's race tracks in the 1960s.

Born in Summit, New Jersey in 1937, Donohue soon showed an aptitude for things mechanical, and graduated from Brown University in mechanical engineering.

He went into industry, but soon his interest in motor racing began to lure him away from his chosen career. He started off with a Chevrolet Corvette which gave him victory in his first-ever event in a hill-climb. He soon moved on to circuit racing in the amateur SCCA (Sports Car Club of America) events and, in 1961, he won the production car category in class E of the SCCA National Championships, with an Elva Courier. He seemed destined to remain in the ranks of the amateurs despite his undoubted talent, but by 1965 he had transferred to single seaters and, when he won the Formula C Championship in a Lotus 20, he came to the notice of Walt Hansgen, then one of America's top sports-car drivers.

Hansgen obtained a drive for Donohue in John Mecom's Ferrari, alongside Hansgen, but the pair gained no great success. However, this drive led to an invitation to join the Ford works team and drive the big 7-litre Mk II sports cars in 1966. Partnered by Hansgen, Donohue drove the Ford into third place at the Daytona 24 Hours of 1966 and followed it up with second place in the Sebring 12 Hours. Tragically, Hansgen was killed at the Le Mans test weekend, but Donohue drove at Le Mans, only to retire.

By this time, Donohue had come to the notice of Roger Penske, the very successful ex-racing driver who had built up a busy Chevrolet dealership in Philadelphia. Penske was running a racing team of his own, and asked Donohue to drive in the new Can-Am Championship for sports cars in a Lola-Chevrolet which was dubbed the Sunoco Lola after the team's sponsor. Donohue was immediately successful, for he finished fifth in his first outing at Bridgehampton, then won the Mosport round and followed up with two fourth places at Laguna Seca and Riverside and a third place at Las Vegas. His points total brought him second place to John Surtees in the Can-Am Championship.

For 1967, Donohue stayed with the Penske team, but less success came his way because the McLaren team was beginning its annihilation of the American stars. However, he placed the Lola second at Road America and third at Riverside, and was leading the final round at Las Vegas when his car ran out of fuel. He also drove for the

Above: Mark Donohue, one of the world's most talented engineers and drivers

Ford team in a few of the World Sports Car Championship races, but his only finish was at Le Mans where he came in fourth, partnered by Bruce McLaren. During 1967, he also won the less prestigious US Road Racing Championship in the Penske Lola.

By 1968, Penske and Donohue had discovered that they worked well together, for Donohue, with his engineering background, had become a fine test driver, while Penske insisted on immaculate preparation of his cars. Penske had been nicknamed 'God' by American journalists while Donohue became known as 'Captain Nice' because of his unfailing good manners and pleasant outlook, as well as his 'all-American boy' chubby good looks and crew-cut hair style. Such was the bond between the two, that Donohue stayed with the Penske team until he retired.

The 1968 season was busy for Donohue, as he drove the Penske Chevrolet Camaro in Trans-Am saloon car races, winning no less than ten of the thirteen events, which gave him the Championship. He also raced a McLaren M6A in the Can-Am series, winning the Bridgehampton round, finishing second at Riverside and third at both Edmonton and Road America. If he had won the final round at Las Vegas he could have clinched the Can-Am title, but his car refused to start on the grid. As well as winning the US Road Racing Championship again in the

Lola, he took the Penske Camaro to the Daytona 24 Hours and finished 12th, then finished third at Sebring, both times co-driven by Craig Fisher.

By 1969, Roger Penske had decided he could not hope to beat the McLaren team in Can-Am racing, so he decided to switch his attention to Indianapolis. Donohue drove the new Lola T152 four-wheel-drive car, powered by a turbocharged Offenhauser engine. Despite never having been to Indianapolis before, he qualified fourth fastest and finished the race in seventh place to win the Rookie of the Year award. He also drove a Camaro to six victories in the Trans-Am series, to clinch the title for Chevrolet again, and teamed up with Chuck Parsons to win the Daytona 24 Hours in Penske's Lola coupé.

The Penske team transferred their allegiance to the American Motors Javelin for the 1970 Trans-Am series, and Donohue picked up three wins and three seconds to take second place to Parnelli Jones' Mustang in the Championship. At Indianapolis, he drove a Lola T153-Ford and finished in a fine second place on the same lap as the winner, Al Unser, earning over £30,000 for the team. Noting the increasing interest in Formula A racing in America, which is the equivalent of Europe's Formula 5000, Penske entered a Lola T192-Chevrolet for the last few races of the Continental Championship. Donohue showed that he was perfectly at home in a big single-seater on a road course by winning at Sebring and Mosport, and finished third at Mid-Ohio.

For 1971, the Penske team took on a new project by rebuilding a 512M Ferrari sports car. This was immaculately prepared to Penske's high standards and, co-driving with Britain's David Hobbs, Donohue finished third at Daytona and sixth at Sebring, but retired at Le Mans when the engine seized. In the Trans-Am series, Donohue again drove the Javelin, and this time won the Championship for American Motors.

Penske acquired a McLaren M16 for Indianapolis, and with it Donohue led the race, but eventually had to retire with gearbox trouble. However, the team took in more USAC Indianapolis-style races and Donohue won the Pocono 500 mile race in the McLaren, but ran out of fuel while leading the California 500 race. To get a taste of Formula One racing, Donohue drove a McLaren M19 in the Canadian Grand Prix towards the end of 1971, and finished a comfortable third in his first ever Formula One race.

For 1972, Roger Penske arranged to use the very powerful turbo-charged 917/10 Porsche in Can-Am racing. Donohue started off with a second place at Mosport, but was then injured in a practice crash which kept him out of racing until October. However, before the crash, he had taken part in the Indianapolis 500 and won the race in an exciting finish when he took the lead with only 13 of the 200 laps left. He was driving the Penske Sunoco McLaren M16B, powered, once again, by a turbo-charged Offenhauser engine.

After recovering from his injuries, Donohue showed that he had lost none of his skill, for he won the Edmonton Can-Am race and followed up by finishing second to team mate George Follmer at Laguna Seca and third at Riverside. Even though he missed five Can-Am races, Donohue still finished fourth in the Championship points table.

In 1973, the Penske team, affectionately known as the 'Penske Panzers', had the use of improved Porsche 917/30 turbocharged Can-Am cars, the 5.4-litre engines of which gave over 1000 bhp, making them almost certainly the most powerful road-racing cars ever used. Donohue ran away with the Can-Am Championship, winning the races at Watkins Glen, Mid-Ohio, Elkhart Lake, Edmonton, Laguna Seca and Riverside. It was said that the 917/30 was so fast that Donohue purposely drove 'slowly', just to make the races more interesting. He would have won the remaining two races, but a collision in one race dropped him to seventh and a fuel leak in the other slowed him slightly and he finally managed to finish second.

Mark also contested Indianapolis again that year in an Eagle-Offenhauser, but he retired with piston failure. He also had a few races in a Formula A Lola, powered by an American Motors V8, but the engine was not very powerful and his best place was second at Seattle. With George Follmer as co-driver, he took a Porsche 911 Carrera to sixth place in the Watkins Glen six-hour race and, driving a standard Porsche 911 Carrera, he won the special Race of Champions series laid on at the top US circuits for top racing drivers, in late 1973 and early 1974.

This was Donohue's last race, for he had announced his impending retirement during the previous November. However, he remained with Penske as manager of his racing team, especially to look after its first venture into Formula One racing in late 1974.   MT

Below: Donohue climbs into the Penske Sunoco Ferrari 512 that he and David Hobbs drove to third place at Daytona in 1971

The quarter mile dash

In 1950, the sport of drag racing was started in order to keep young American tearaways from racing their cars on the public roads. Today, drag racing is a highly sophisticated business with huge crowds watching tremendously powerful and expensive cars travelling at speeds in excess of 200mph and setting quarter-mile times of six seconds or less

Above: drivers who race open, front-engined dragsters wear special clothing and breathing gear in case the engine explodes and spurts burning oil into the car's slipstream and the driver's face

Left: a pro-stock Camaro 'bleaching out'

ANYONE WHO INCLUDES HIMSELF among the ranks of Britain's motor-racing enthusiasts will have noticed, over the past few years, that the branch of the sport known as drag racing has risen considerably in popularity. Few of the more dyed-in-the-wool circuit-racing fans, though, will have much concept of the development and history of drag racing because, in England at least, it has been rather starved of publicity by the media. However, by 1974, after more than ten years and many thousands of high-speed quarter miles, it was beginning to gain regular reports in the motor-sporting press.

The definition of the sport is quite simple: it is a timed speed contest between two cars over one-quarter of a mile. The cars start together when a green light shows, and the one that gets to the other end of the 'strip' first is the winner. At face value, that might sound like no sport at all—a simple acceleration test over a flat, straight quarter-mile tarmac strip does not involve many of the skills that one conventionally associates with the great exponents of circuit racing. The drag-strip, though, is a breeding ground for abilities of a rather different nature. Like all motor sports, the race really starts in the engine/chassis-building workshops, where new designs, tricks and methods are constantly being tried out. The success of these is borne out by the results, and nowhere has there been more amazing progress than in drag racing. In America in 1950, which was the year in which the first hint of any organised drag racing was seen, a time of 17 seconds for the quarter was regarded as very good. In 1974, several top dragsters were regularly recording times of under six seconds, while jet-engined cars were running times of under five seconds with speeds of over 300 mph!

Once the two contestants are out there side by side on the start line, though, the only things that will get one man through the timing lights at the far end of the strip first are reactions, skill and more than a little bravery, assuming that both cars are producing similar horsepower. Fast reactions are the first things needed. The timing lights in each lane usually have seven bulbs, one above the other: two red ones at the top that show when both cars are 'staged' or lined up properly, and then a timed rundown sequence of orange, orange, orange and then green. The experienced drag racer is already pushing his foot to the floor as the green comes on, but if he crosses the start line before it shows, one more red bulb is illuminated and he loses by default.

The skill comes in knowing the precise combination of clutch and throttle that will move the car off the line quickly and cleanly without spinning the wheels too much or allowing the car to 'bog' down through releasing the clutch too quickly or not using enough

throttle, and also in knowing at what precise moment to change gear and how to lose a minimum of engine revolutions while so doing. Bravery? Well, the fastest cars, early in 1974, were reaching terminal speeds of close on 250 mph and they were long, narrow cars with thin motor-cycle tyres at the front, and a consequent lack of good handling characteristics in accident situations. Drag-racing accidents are always dramatic, but fortunately the fatality rate is very low.

In the early days of the sport there were no classes—you could drive your car to the strip and, as long as it had four wheels and an engine, it could run against anything else. Today, slight differences exist between the many classes used in America and those employed in England, but generally speaking, the main classes are similar in outline. The slowest and cheapest class, which is also the backbone of the sport, consists of cars loosely described as 'Street'. These must be cars basically in standard road-going trim, although a great deal of work is permitted on the engines. The suspension, steering, engine position and dimensions of the

Above: Clive Skilton, the 1973 National Drag Racing Champion, *inset,* and his American-bought, Keith Black-engined top fueler leaving the line just as the 'Xmas tree' flashes the green light. Note how the tyres crinkle as the enormous amount of torque is transmitted to the road. Note also the car's mid-engine layout, the parachute mounted above the large differential and the plate on the left-hand front wheel that ensures a clean break as the car passes the timing lights

Far left: an early-1956 aero-engined dragster

Left centre: the massive Chrysler-supercharged engine that gives driver Dennis Priddle about 1500 bhp to use

Near left: by far the best way to slow a drag racer from high speed is a parachute. Such devices are obligatory on all cars that have speeds of over 150 mph

car are not allowed to be modified, although, in certain cases, they may be supplemented by items like traction bars, roll cages, special dampers and so on. The faster cars in the street class are currently returning times in the region of twelve seconds.

Then there are the Pro-Stocks, the deceptive cars that look like regular saloons but, in fact, have glass-fibre body panels and far more powerful engines. Certain body modifications are permitted, and supercharging is commonplace. The body dimensions must remain basically as on the production car, but the light weight of those glassfibre panels, combined with the staggering horsepower outputs, makes times of 8 or 9 seconds quite regular occurrences. Just to give you some idea of how that compares, the V12 E-type Jaguar would take 14.5 seconds to cover the same distance!

Even faster are the powerful Competition Altered cars. These are short-wheelbase vehicles with open glassfibre bodies, usually based on cut-down model T replica shells. Their shortness renders them hard to

control and, wherever they race, the crowd can be assured of some dramatic action. They are also extremely fast, turning in top speeds of over 180 mph and burning up that quarter mile in 7–8 seconds.

Almost certainly the most popular cars are those running in the Funny Car class. These incredibly fast machines, yet again, look quite similar to the kind of car any American earning a reasonable salary could walk right into a car showroom and purchase. In reality, they are as different as rats and ratatouille. For a start, the whole car body is made of glassfibre, not just a few panels, and it is all in one piece, too; there are no opening doors or boots, and the only way to work on the engine is to lift the entire front end of the bodywork up off the chassis. Inside, there is just a single seat encased in aluminium panels and a few strange-looking levers. The engine, usually about seven or eight litres of fuel-injected and supercharged Chrysler-based hardware putting out around 1600–1700 bhp, is mounted well-back in the chassis, half in and half out of the passenger compartment. The rear

Above: a top fueler 'burning out'. An inflammable liquid is spread under the rear wheels of the car and ignited, then the driver spins the wheels so they rub in the hot fluid and get 'sticky', thus giving the car better traction. This method has now been outlawed in America where it was said to be too dangerous. In 1974 in England, it was still practised, although pouring bleach under the wheels proved just as effective, the bleach giving excellent traction

speeds in excess of 250 mph, all that from a standing start in just one quarter of a mile.

How did it all start? Well, it goes almost without saying that drag racing was primarily an American invention and, although it is almost impossible to pin down a time and a place where and when drag racing actually started, it is generally accepted that the first organised meeting took place in Santa Ana, California, in July 1950. It seems that all over California that year, kids with tuned cars had been racing their hot rods on the streets, and it was getting just a little dangerous, with one group in particular getting their fun by jumping red lights at more than 90 mph! The police tried to crack down on it, but without much success—hot-rodding was growing so fast that there were almost as many hot rods as patrol cars. So, belive it or not, in a last desperate attempt to get them off the streets, the California Highway patrol organised a meeting at Orange County Airport where the kids could race each other till their crankshafts cracked. It was a terrific success—all the police had to do was to rule that anybody who had committed serious traffic offences could not race there, and suddenly California's streets were a lot safer.

The National Hot Rod Association of America was formed by a man called Wally Parks who, in 1974, was still the NHRA's President. The other main body is the American Hot Rod Association (AHRA). Parks and one other man are together mainly responsible for the popularity of drag racing through the years. The other man's name is Don Garlits, who has been racing dragsters every year since 1953! Not only did he still race, but he was still the fastest man on the strip in '74—at the end of 1973, he was seen to demoralise his opposition at the Supernational Championships in California by unloading his car and straight away going out on the dragstrip to stop the timing clocks at 5.80 seconds, considerably faster than anyone had ever been before! Garlits has become a legend among drag racers, and there is not a drag-racing fan in the world who does not know his name. He has had a few bad accidents—been burned badly more than once and lost a part of his foot on one occasion, but he still dominates the scene in a way that no circuit racer has ever done.

In 1964, Garlits and another American called Tommy Ivo came over to England to give a series of exhibition races to anyone interested enough to show up. It wasn't the first time drag racing had been seen in England; a club had been formed as early as 1960, and there was a hard core of enthusiastic fans and drivers. Sydney Allard, manufacturer of the famous Allard cars, was among the early drivers, and he also contributed greatly to the organisation of British drag racing in the early days. 1964, though, was the year it all started to get off the ground in England; over 20,000 people turned up to watch the two Americans and the British competitors at Blackbushe Airfield in Surrey that summer. The following year, a larger team of Americans came over, but the tour was plagued with rain. In 1966, more Americans came and, by this time, England had a permanent drag strip at Santa Pod in Bedfordshire.

An interesting footnote is that the more spectacular classes in drag racing, like the fuelers, the Funny Cars, and the Competition Altereds do not run on oil-based fuels. They use methanol, which is a fuel derived from wood alcohol, or a potent mix of a substance called nitro-methane. It's extremely volatile stuff and, in 1974 drag-racing circles, there were moves afoot to get it banned on account of its high cost—one run down the strip in an AA fueler can cost £70—and its tendency to catch fire.   AA

Top: Roy Phelps' 7-litre Chevrolet Stingray. Its engine is so accurately placed in the chassis that the car can quite easily cover the whole ¼-mile on its rear wheels (a full-length 'wheelie'). Although such practice pleases crowds, it badly hampers performance. However, it still manages 'quarters' of under 14 seconds. In fact, the car is not meant to be a serious contender, as the glass floor (enabling the driver to see where he is going when pointing skywards) proves

Above: Swede Arnold Sundqvist's Silver Streak which is powered by a Westinghouse J46 jet engine, late of a Lockheed Starfighter aircraft

wheels are enormously wide, and wrapped around them are huge treadless tyres called slicks. These are run at extremely low pressures—so low in fact that the sidewalls can be seen to wrinkle—to provide maximum traction—and so light is the body that it shakes about like a wobbling jelly when the engine is started, looking strangely flimsy despite the powerful bellow coming from the unsilenced exhausts. The Funny Cars are almost the fastest cars to be seen at dragstrips—they regularly clock speeds of well over 220 mph and record elapsed times of under 6.2 seconds.

In fact, there is only one class that is faster, apart from the unsanctioned rocket devices, and that's the one for what are known as double A fuelers. These are the pure dragsters, the ultimate extension of the sport. The engines they use are similar to those in the Funny Cars but, of course, the low, streamlined bodies are much lighter and present lower frontal areas. Until a few years ago, the engines were usually mounted forward of the driver, approximately halfway along the wheelbase but, in latter years, the trend has been towards rear-engined dragsters, or rails as they are popularly known. This seems to give better weight distribution, as well as affording the driver better vision and a better chance of escaping unscathed should the engine explode, an occurrence that is rare but not unknown. 1973 saw dragsters breaking the six-second barrier for the first time with terminal

Far left: a Competition Altered, based on a British Ford of the 1950s

Left: Midas Touch, a Jaguar XK-engined rod raced in Britain in the mid '60s

Above left: the Funny Cars proved to be the most popular class on both sides of the Atlantic in 1975

Above: a top fueler wrinkles its tyres on take off

Left: a 'slightly modified' Pro Stock Camaro

Above: a Competition Altered car with a Fiat 500 Topolino body

Right: a racing model of 1921, with an in-line eight-cylinder engine of 3 litres

Below: a Duesenberg competition model, photographed at Monza

Below right: the engine of the SJ (a tuned version of the model J)

Bottom: the model A roadster of 1925; it had a 90 bhp engine and was the first American car with hydraulic brakes

A NAME WITH A TOUCH OF MAGIC

In the beginning, the Duesenberg was hampered by its foreign-sounding name.
This name has now become immortal and the cars are among the world's great classics

DUESENBERG—THE VERY NAME has an arrogant ring to it, totally befitting what is arguably the finest motor car to have been built in America. Yet, alongside the luxury cars for which they are now chiefly remembered, the Duesenberg brothers, Fred and August, produced some of the most successful racing cars of their day However, although racing may have improved the breed, there is evidence that it did not much impress those rich enough to buy a Duesenberg.

The Duesenberg family originated in Lippe, Germany, and emigrated to America in the mid 1880s. As teenagers in Iowa in the 1890s, the two brothers started a bicycle business—they had received little formal education—and sometime around 1900 are reputed to have built a clip-on motor unit for one of their cycles. Fred was a natural engineer, and left the cycle shop to join the Thomas B. Jeffery Company at Kenosha, Wisconsin, where they were just switching over from Rambler bicycles to Rambler cars. In 1906, the brothers were in business together again, at Des Moines, Iowa, building a 24 hp, flat-twin car with an epicyclic gearbox and chain final-drive. Finance was provided by a lawyer named Mason, from whom the car took its name.

In 1910, Fred Duesenberg designed a racing-car engine whose horizontal valves were operated from the low-mounted camshaft by long rocker arms known as 'walking beams'. In that year, too, the company

Below: Duesenberg cars were always the epitome of elegance and luxury combined with power and grace. This is the Dual Cowl Phaeton of 1929 which sold for 14,000 dollars

Above: a superb example of the coachbuilder's art is this Duesenberg Victoria Model J of 1931. The car was powered by a straight-eight, twin-overhead-camshaft, 265 bhp, Lycoming engine

Right: a Duesenberg model J convertible tourer. Most Model Js came on the standard wheelbase lengths of 11 ft 10½ in (short) or 12 ft 9½ in (long), although one model was produced on an enormous 14 ft 10 in wheelbase

Right: Erret Lobban Cord could never be accused of soft-selling his products, as this example of Duesenberg advertising, liberally sprinkled with superlatives, shows

changed its name, being taken over by one Fred Maytag (later well known as a washing machine manufacturer), although the racing engines were known as Mason-Duesenbergs up to 1914, implying that Mr Mason (whose son George drove one of these cars at Indianapolis that year) was still backing the racing side of the business.

In 1914, though, the brothers cut loose from their sponsors, and set up in business at St Paul, Minneapolis, building racing cars which were largely similar to the Mason-Duesenbergs, except for a high exhaust pipe curling out of the top of the bonnet; breathing was improved on some 1916 engines by fitting four valves per cylinder instead of two. Many leading drivers raced Duesenbergs during this period—Eddie Rickenbacker, Ralph Mulford, Willie Haupt and Tommy Milton—and by 1916 the marque's reputation was such that the brothers were chosen to produce Bugatti sixteen-cylinder aero-engines for the US Government. They moved into a new factory at Elizabeth, New Jersey, but only 400 or so Bugatti engines were built in 1918–19, before the project was abandoned due to the power unit's unreliability.

The Duesenbergs sold their factory to John North Willys, and went back to building cars. At first, they worked in the garage of Fred's home in Elizabeth, then they rented a local workshop, where a new power unit, obviously inspired by their work on the Bugatti U-16 engine (in effect, two straight-eights side by side), was developed. This was a straight-eight of 4.26 litres, which was fitted into a modified racing-car chassis; Tommy Milton drove this car in the 1919 Indianapolis 500, retiring after 49 laps with a broken con-rod.

DUESENBERG

It is a monumental answer to wealthy America's
insistent demand for the best that modern engineering
and artistic ability can provide .... Equally it is a tribute to the
widely-recognized engineering genius of FRED S. DUESENBERG, its designer,
and to E. L. CORD, its sponsor, for these men in one imaginative
stroke have snatched from the far future an automobile which
is years ahead and therefore incomparably superior
to any other car which may be bought today.

The old four-cylinder, walking-beam design was sold to Rochester Motors, who produced these power units for such assembled quality cars as the Roamer (which had a fake-Rolls radiator), the ReVere and Biddle, until 1923–24.

Duesenberg built a series of straight-eight racing cars for the 1920 season, then began work on two new

and exciting projects. The first was a sixteen-cylinder car with two 4.9-litre straight-eights mounted side-by-side; Tommy Milton set up an unofficial world land speed record of 156.05 mph with this car at Daytona in April 1920. More important, though, was the company's first passenger car, which had a 4.26-litre engine similar to the racing units (but with two valves per cylinder instead of three). This was completed in time to be displayed at the 1920 New York Salon.

This was the first production straight-eight on the American market, and also the first to feature four-wheel hydraulic braking. In the former respect, it was three years ahead of the rest of the market, while the brake layout was even more advanced. Valves were operated by a single overhead camshaft, and the engine design made extensive use of aluminium; it also pioneered alloy pistons in America, though cast-iron units were available for conservative buyers.

Only a handful of prototypes were built before Duesenberg moved into an impressive new factory, in Indianapolis, which could cope with all aspects of car production. Contrary to contemporary American practice, the Duesenberg brothers built their own engines and most other mechanical components; the three-bearing crankshaft was notably rigid, and carefully balanced to eliminate vibration.

At the time of the straight-eight's introduction, the racing models had already established 66 American records on the Sheepshead Bay Board Speedway, and the passenger version of the racer was naturally billed as 'The World's Champion Automobile—built to outclass, outrun and outlast any car on the road'. It followed that much testing of the production models

was carried out on the Indianapolis Speedway, including stunts such as a three-week non-stop run (apart from halts to change tyres and drivers and to refuel) covering 18,032 miles, and a simulated high-speed dash across the United States without stopping (the car was refuelled on the move but, in fact, had to stop twice to change tyres). The 3155-mile run took just 50 hours 21 minutes, an average speed of 62.63 mph, and a remarkable achievement for a completely standard car with relatively weighty five-passenger touring coachwork on a normal chassis.

Even more impressive was the marque's victory in the 1921 French Grand Prix, a feat which has not so far been repeated by any other American manufacturer. Jimmy Murphy's car, aided by its four-wheel braking, beat the best cars and drivers that Europe had to offer on the Le Mans circuit: despite the poor road surface and flying stones, Murphy averaged 78.1 mph over the 322-mile race—10 mph faster than the quickest pre-war average and, indeed, faster than many French GPs over the following decade (for instance, Caracciola's Mercedes won the 1935 French GP at 77.42 mph over a similar distance on the far smoother Montlhéry circuit).

However, this victory, and other track achievements such as the Duesenberg first place at Indianapolis in 1924 (plus the marque's many other successes, which culminated in a second Indianapolis win and the AAA Championship in 1926), failed to have any great effect on passenger car sales. For one thing, the marque's Teutonic-sounding name counted against it in the years immediately following the Armistice; more importantly, while to European motorists a racing

Above: a fine specimen of the Model J, this being the convertible roadster version. The Model J had a top speed of 116 mph and its chassis price was 8500 dollars. The car was fitted with hydraulic brakes all round and much of the body was made of aluminium. On this chassis, many of America's finest coachbuilders constructed their greatest bodies and often the total price of a completed car was over 20,000 dollars

pedigree was indicative of high engineering standards and a good road performance, to the Americans rich enough to afford a Duesenberg, racing cars meant noise, smell and smoke, and though the Duesenberg Straight Eight was guilty of none of these vices, it was credited with them by association.

Sales, therefore, were not as good as they should have been; although poor body styling is a criticism sometimes levelled against the 1921–26 Duesenbergs, they were as good in this respect as most of their contemporaries, the plain fact of the matter being that American coachbuilders of the 1920s lacked the flair of their European counterparts, both in overall conception and in the treatment of details and accessories.

Also, Fred Duesenberg was an engineer first and a financier a long way after. He could, it is said, work out the dimensions of key components, like connecting rods, by eye, and arrive within one or two thousandths of an inch of the carefully stress-calculated computations of engineers with more formal training. What is more, he fully expected every member of his staff to work the same long hours as himself.

Small wonder, then, that the marque's *succès d'éstime* was not reflected in its bank balance, and that Straight Eight production totalled no more than 500–650 units in the model's six-year life. In 1926, the company was taken over by that up-and-coming entrepreneur, Erret Lobban Cord (he died at the beginning of 1974), who immediately instituted a programme of styling changes. Wisely, however, he left Fred and August in charge of engineering, and all he insisted on was that the brothers should produce a new car which, in terms of style, engineering and sheer panache, should rival the best the world had to offer. In December 1928, they revealed the result of their labours to the public—it was, they claimed, 'The World's Finest Car', the Model J Duesenberg. Its 6.9-litre power unit was built by another Cord subsidiary, Lycoming, well known as suppliers of proprietary engines; however, this was no off-the-shelf side-valve six, but a race-bred straight-eight with twin overhead camshafts operating four valves per cylinder. Claimed output was 265 bhp, twice that of any other American passenger car. The model J had a top speed in the region of 116 mph and its chassis price was $8,500.

The engine was rubber-mounted in a chassis of exceptional rigidity; frame side-members were $8\frac{1}{2}$ inches deep, and there were six cross-members plus diagonal bracing. Of course, much use was made of aluminium, and the car had hydraulic brakes all round (with variable servo assistance from 1929 on). Hardly in line with the best European practice were the long, willowy central gear lever and handbrake, but the standard instrumentation was obviously designed to impress the most gadget-conscious of owners. Across the somewhat spartan fascia were scattered 150 mph speedometer, altimeter, barometer, brake-pressure gauge, tachometer, ammeter, oil-pressure gauge, combination clock and stop-clock, and a complex set of lights operated by a train of timing wheels which drove a device known as the 'timing box' under the bonnet. Every 75 miles, the box automatically lubricated all the chassis greasing points; a red light glowed when it was working, a green one when its lubricant reservoir needed refilling. Every 700 miles, a third light exhorted the owner to have the engine oil changed while, at 1400 mile intervals, the fourth light acted as an *aide-memoire* to have the battery water level checked at the nearest service station.

On this chassis, the finest coachbuilders of America and Europe—Murphy, Derham, Bohmann & Schwartz, Hibbard & Darrin, Barker, Letourneur & Marchand,

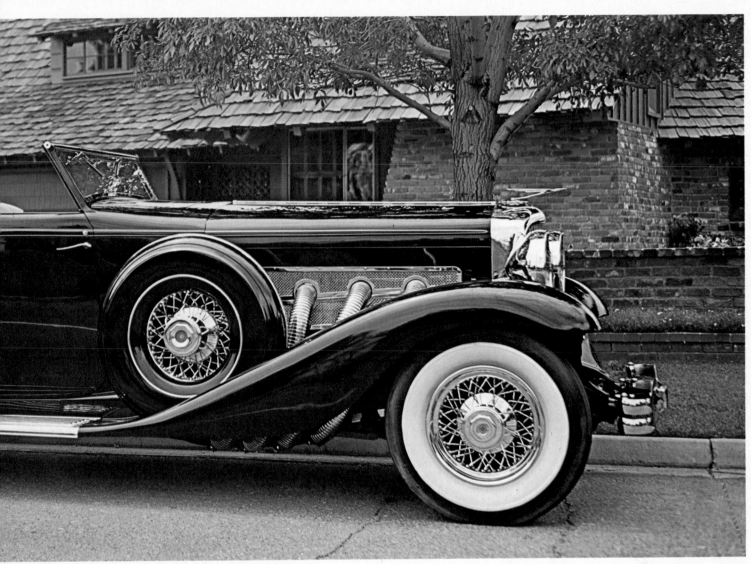

Graber, D'Ieteren Frères, Gurney Nutting and Weymann—constructed their finest bodies, bringing the total cost of the car, as the model name of one convertible phaeton version reminded the world, to 'Twenty Grand', give or take a few thousand dollars.

Most Model Js came on the standard wheelbase lengths of 11 ft 10½ in (short) or 12 ft 9½ in (long), though Father Divine, an evangelist, ordered his Duesenberg with a whopping 14 ft 10 in wheelbase, and graced it with the name *Throne Car*.

The old Straight-Eight engine wasn't entirely abandoned after the Model J appeared: the introduction of the 'Junk Formula' for stock engines, at Indianapolis in 1930, saw the emergence of many Duesenberg-engined racers, although few, if any, raced under their marque name, preferring such patronymics as *Wonder Bread Special*.

The rise of the Model J Duesenberg is all the more remarkable when one considers that, at the time the model was on the market, there was a world depression, but the Duesenberg *clientèle* was made up of those who were above mere details like the collapse of the stock market; so it is perhaps not so curious that the company introduced an even more flamboyant model in 1932, when the American car market was virtually on its knees.

This was the SJ, which added a centrifugal supercharger spinning at five times crankshaft speed to boost the power output to a claimed 320 bhp and the top speed to almost 130 mph.

Above: in 1932, the American car market was on its knees and it was during this year that Duesenberg chose to introduce their SJ model. Against all the odds, the SJ survived and went on to become one of the world's great classic cars. Fitted with a supercharger, the engine produced 320 bhp and the car had a claimed top speed of almost 130 mph

Left: yet another version of Duesenberg's famous SJ model; this is a 1932 convertible tourer

571

The bulk of the blower installation made it impossible to accommodate the standard exhaust system under the bonnet, so Duesenberg brought the exhausts out through the bonnet sides in four chromed flexible downpipes. Outside exhausts were a relatively common styling trick in Europe (where the Duesenberg cost more than either Rolls-Royce or Hispano-Suiza), but came as a novelty on the American market. There were even owners of the 'unblown' J who had the external plumbing fitted to make their cars look more exotic. Rarest of all the Duesenbergs was the SSJ, built on the 'ultra-short' (10 ft 5 in) wheelbase; only two were made, one for Clark Gable and one for Gary Cooper, both famous actors.

Greta Garbo owned a Duesenberg, too; so did Marion Davies, Mae West, Joe E. Brown and William Randolph Hearst. Royal customers included King Alfonso XIII of Spain, King Victor Emmanuel of Italy, Queen Marie of Yugoslavia and Prince Nicholas of Romania, who raced one of his three Model Js at Le Mans, in 1933, 1934 and 1935, with an outstanding lack of success.

However, even all the top customers in the world could not save Duesenberg. Fate had already claimed Fred Duesenberg, killed in 1932 at the wheel of an early SJ, and now the break-up of the Cord empire would destroy the company he had headed. The first indication that the end was near had come in 1935 when the final shipment of 25 Duesenberg engines had been received from Lycoming; lack of a future sales programme precluded further production of power units in the Lycoming factory.

The company showed its 1937 models at New York and Chicago as though all was well, but then the Cord bubble burst, and the purchasers of the group's assets decided to curtail car production. The Duesenberg factory was bought by local truck builders Marmon-Herrington, one last chassis was assembled to the order of a rich German client by August Duesenberg and his devoted workmen in Chicago, and a new spares and service company was specially created in Auburn, Indiana, during 1938, for owners of Auburn, Cord and Duesenberg cars.

The Duesenberg name lived on, though. In 1947, Marshall Merkes of Chicago bought the company's remaining assets and employed August Duesenberg to design a new straight-eight. It was to have had fuel-injection and custom coachwork, but the realisation that the basic price would be at least $25,000 caused the project to be abandoned. August Duesen-

berg, founder of this legendary concern, died of a heart attack in 1955, aged 76.

In mid 1965, came news of another attempt to revive the marque, this time as a completely modern luxury car with contemporary Detroit styling, fronted by an updated version of the Duesenberg radiator grille. Styled by Ghia and over 24 feet long, the Chrysler-powered 1966 Duesenberg was America's biggest four-door sedan, but the price tag of around $20,000 was more than the customers were prepared to pay, and only one car was built. Then came the revival of the SSJ, by another firm, the Duesenberg Corporation of Gardena, California, that was still in production in early 1974. Based on a Dodge truck chassis, with commercial-vehicle suspension, but curiously with almost the same SSJ wheelbase, at 10 ft 8 in, it was powered by a supercharged Chrysler engine producing 500 bhp. The latter-day SSJ was an attempt to recapture the mystical aura of its earlier namesake (the car still had the mass of instruments and gauges), but, with the company announcing that the price was 'on application', the car could probably only be afforded by modern Gary Coopers.

Despite these latter-day failures, the Duesenberg name still carries the old magic—quite an achievement when you realise that total output of Straight-Eights, Js and SJs amounts to little more than a thousand cars in eighteen years. Nowadays, the large car manufacturers feel themselves unsuccessful if they turn out so few examples of their products in a day, the demand being so great. DBW

Above: an eight-cylinder, 3-litre Duesenberg racing car pictured during tests at Monza in 1921. The car, driven by Jimmy Murphy, scored a great victory at the French Grand Prix that year, beating the best cars and drivers that Europe had to offer

Below: this striking Duesenberg Model J of 1933 is fitted with a two-seater body built by the Weymann company, one of motoring history's most famous coach-building concerns

MOTORING ECCENTRICITIES

Although Dunkley never produced any show-stopping products, they certainly could not be accused of being unimaginative

MOTORISTS OF THE MID 1890s were an uncritical breed: mechanical monstrosities like the Pennington Torpedo were accepted without demur, and it had to be a pretty unusual car for the motoring press to notice that it had any shortcomings. Such a car was built in 1896 by Dunkley of Birmingham. For one thing, its wheels were arranged in diamond formation, the centre pair driving, the outer, smaller single wheels steering. While this layout has been followed by other experimenters throughout motoring history, the Dunkley was unique in that the chassis was so arranged that only one of the steering wheels touched the ground. Which one it was, apparently, depended on whether the driver or his rearward-facing passenger was the heavier!

To make it more complicated, both driver and passenger had steering tillers, while the brake lever was entrusted to the passenger, who could not see which way the vehicle was going without twisting himself around.

Even the motive power was unorthodox, for the Dunkley was designed to run on coal gas. Hardly surprisingly, the company's attempt to market this vehicle lasted no longer than the howls of derision which greeted its appearance.

In 1901, Dunkley tried again. This time the company offered the public a range of 'Patent Self-charging Gas Motor Cars', which took their supply of gas from any ordinary gas pipe or street lamp post—although, whether the local gas company would give such a procedure their blessing was left to the customer's imagination!

Typical of the breed was the Dunkley's number 3, shown at the 1902 Agricultural Hall Motor Exhibition run by that moustachioed extrovert, Charles Cordingley.

The number 3 was a curious tandem two-seater, with the driver in the rear seat. It carried storage tanks holding enough gas for a 100-mile run (so it was claimed—the tanks looked suspiciously small). These were filled by a patent double-acting gas compressor, which was combined in some way with the car's power unit. This consisted of patent twin engines running together or uncoupled at will by the driver; there were two forward speeds plus reverse. For some mysterious reason, there was a patent reversible steering handle.

Amazingly, this curious vehicle was, in theory at any rate, on the market for several years, though sales must have been minimal.

Dunkley, it seems, were convinced that the motor vehicle had a future, even if their opinion of what constituted a winning design was diametrically opposed to the general view for, in 1911, they made a fourth attempt to break into the big time. This was their most conventional vehicle, a cyclecar named the Alvechurch after their factory, Alvechurch Works, Bradford Street, Birmingham, England. It was a twin-cylinder-Matchless-engined creation, of which history only records that its driving belts slipped badly and only two examples were built.

This venture into conventionality must have frightened Dunkley off for, until 1923, they devoted themselves to their main activity, the manufacture of prams (motor-cycle sidecars, plus a range of motor cycles, were sidelines).

In 1923, Dunkley made the decision which was to earn them immortality: to produce a motor pram. The heart of this was a unit called the Pramotor, which was basically a scooter with the front wheel missing. This one-wheeled power pack could be fastened to the rear of any Dunkley pram: Nanny stood astride the rear wheel, controlling the outfit's

hectic progress with twin handlebars bolted to the back of the pram.

Power units were originally all 1 hp, horizontal, single-cylinder two-strokes, with bore and stroke dimensions of 2 in × 2 in. There was only one gear (two-speed gearing appeared a year later), but there was a kick starter and a hand-controlled clutch. Prices ranged from 40 guineas for the Dunkley Model 20 Pramotor outfit, to 135 guineas for the Saloon Pramotor with $26 \times 2\frac{1}{2}$ in Palmer Cord motor tyres. This odd little vehicle, which looked like a five-wheeled Easter Egg, had proper Ackermann steering, mudguards and running boards, and cost only £24 less than a complete Austin Seven. Or, indeed, as much as a Model T Ford!

An economy Pramotor appeared in 1924, with one gear, and no clutch or kick-starter: presumably Alice had to bump-start Christopher Robin on his motorised walkies!

For sporting Nannies there was now the option of a $2\frac{3}{4}$ hp engine—a 750 cc two-stroke single—which at 75 guineas promised performance far beyond the roadholding capabilities of the average perambulator, for the Pramotors were prohibited by law from using public footpaths or poop-pooping through the parks. They had to mix it on the open road with more conventional, more controllable vehicles.

Fortunately, perhaps, for the infant mortality statistics, sales of Pramotors were low: but when production ceased in 1925, the motoring scene was deprived of one of its spectacular eccentricities. DBW

The number 3 was shown at the 1902 Agricultural Hall Motor Exhibition. It was a tandem two-seater with the driver sitting at the rear

RIDING ON AIR

John Boyd Dunlop is generally considered to be the father of the pneumatic tyre as we know it today

IF JOHN BOYD DUNLOP had been a less indulgent father, we might still be bumping round in solid-tyred vehicles. An unlikely hypothesis, but one with more than a grain of truth.

Dunlop was born in 1840 in the little Ayrshire village of Dreghorn. He took a degree in veterinary surgery at Edinburgh University at the age of nineteen, and by the 1880s had a successful practice in Belfast, where he had settled in 1867. He also had a son, Johnny, aged about ten, on whom he obviously doted, for he had bought the boy a little chain-driven tricycle on which to ride to school.

Johnny, however, was a typical small boy, and complained that the tricycle was not comfortable enough: the solid tyres, he claimed, jarred at him as he rode over the stony streets.

So Dunlop set about finding some way of easing the road shocks. Inspired, possibly, by memories from his Edinburgh days of 'aerial wheels' invented by the Scottish engineer R. W. Thomson in 1845, he cut two discs of wood. Round one of them he fitted an inflated sheet-rubber air tube, held in place by a strip of canvas nailed to the wooden 'wheel'. He bowled the two discs along the ground, and found that the one with the inflated tyre ran farther than the plain one.

This, then, was the answer to Johnny's problem, and Dunlop decided to fit inflatable tyres to the rear wheels of the boy's tricycle. The rim was a circular strip of thin wood from a round cheese box, the tube was made from rubber sheeting stuck with solution and held to the rim by a spiral of canvas wound between the spokes; a tread of vulcanised rubber protected the tube from punctures.

He found that not only did these 'pneumatic tyres' (which were inflated, through a non-return valve, by a football pump) ease the road shocks, but also made it far easier to pedal the tricycle, which just rolled over the irregularities.

Dunlop saw that there might be commercial possibilities in the idea and, on 23 July 1888, took out a patent at Belfast for a 'chamber of rubber or other suitable material to contain air under pressure or otherwise, fastened to the rim by the most convenient method'.

Now he looked around for someone who would assist him in his experiments, and called on a firm of Belfast cycle agents, R. W. Edlin and Finlay Sinclair. They were naturally sceptical—after all Dunlop couldn't even ride a bicycle—so Dunlop put his invention to a simple test.

Young Johnny challenged Edlin's eighteen-year-old son to a race—pneumatic-tyred tricycle against solid-tyred bicycle—and won. Convinced, Edlin and Sinclair built some cycles with specially widened forks to take the new tyres. Dunlop asked them to make the front wheel of 28 inches diameter and the rear wheel of 34 inches.

'I was afraid the rear wheel, having to carry the principle weight of the rider and withstand the driving strain, would not wear well unless made large,' he wrote.

Although Edlin and Sinclair were impressed, Dunlop could not interest the big cycle companies in the pneumatic tyres, as they had huge stocks of components suitable only for solid-tyred machines, and were reluctant to take up an invention that would render their products obsolete overnight.

Racing cyclists, however, had no vested interests to protect, and Dunlop immediately aroused their curiosity by proclaiming that the pneumatic tyre would increase the speed of their machines. In the autumn of 1888, he arranged for local racing cyclists to try a pneumatic tyre at the Ormeau Park Track in Belfast. Among those who came along was William Hume of the Belfast Cruisers Cycle Club, who had just retired from competition after a fall from his high-wheeled ordinary bicycle.

After trying Dunlop's pneumatic, he changed his mind, and decided to start racing again, using the new tyre. Edlin and Sinclair built him a racing cycle, but many events then were closed to all but solid-tyred machines. The first contest for which his bicycle was eligible was the Belfast Queen's College Sports, in 1889. Hume won all four races in which he was entered, beating three of the famous Du Cros brothers —Alfred, Willie and Harvey—who, at that time, were regarded as virtually invincible on their ordinaries.

In fact, the Du Cros brothers were so convinced that they stood no chance against Hume, that they took the train home to Dublin without waiting for the conclusion of the race meeting.

To preserve family honour, a return match was arranged between Hume and the most accomplished cyclist of the six young Du Cros brothers—Arthur—a fortnight later at the North of Ireland Cricket Club Sports, on the same grass track course as before.

This time, the ground was hard and dry, and Du

Left and right: John Boyd Dunlop, the man who put motoring comfortably on four wheels. Dunlop was one of the many people who transformed motoring from a crude pastime for the brave to a mode of transport perfectly acceptable in luxury and comfort. Also, like so many of his counter-parts, Dunlop did not profit from his invention, but, he had at least got his name associated with the company

Cros's solid-tyred Humber came in ahead of Hume, but the closeness of the match convinced Harvey Du Cros senior that there was 'more than mere air in the inflated tyre', and he arranged a meeting with Dunlop to discuss marketing the pneumatic tyre commercially.

A few weeks later, the pneumatic tyre was introduced to England, at the Liverpool Police Sports. Again, William Hume was the rider and, the moment he appeared on the field, a roar of contemptuous laughter went up. Shouts of derision—'pudding wheels . . . mud cart . . . steam roller . . . cartwheels'— went up, for none of the spectators had ever seen anything like the 2-inch-section tyres fitted to the 'Humeatic' bicycle.

'If I'd known you were going to ride a machine like that old home-made Irish bicycle,' jeered the handicapper, 'I'd have put you on a longer mark.'

However, when Hume won the one-mile and three-mile open handicaps with ease, the laughter turned to amazement. When the machine was put on display in the window of a cycle store in Lime Street, Liverpool, after the race, the crowds overflowed the pavement onto the road, and the police had to be called in to keep order.

The time was now ripe to market the invention. In November 1889, the prospectus of the Pneumatic Tyre Company was issued and within two years R. J. Mecredy could write that 'the pneumatic tyre had thoroughly revolutionised the cycling trade', for the pneumatic tyre was admirably suited to the recently introduced small-wheeled safety bicycle, and these two novelties formed a powerful sales combination.

Though John Boyd Dunlop's image and superscription were used in promoting the new tyre, he had no share in its commercial success, for he had sold his patent for £700 to Harvey Du Cros; indeed, when the Dunlop Pneumatic Tyre Company held a dinner at London's Hotel Metropole a decade later, to celebrate the tenth anniversary of the pneumatic tyre, John Boyd Dunlop's name was not among the guests of honour— it was Harvey Du Cros to whom they drank a toast.

The Dunlop Company was just one of those concerns which, during the great cycle boom of the 1890s, was floated for vast sums by that king among company promotors, Terah Hooley. Hooley gained control of Dunlop for £3 million, and resold it for £5 million in one of the major coups of his flamboyant career.

However, the original Dunlop tyre was far from perfect. Its biggest disadvantage was that it was cemented on to the rim, which made repairing punctures a major task. As early as 1889, the Michelin brothers of Clermont-Ferrand, France, had devised a detachable pneumatic to overcome this problem, thus founding France's major tyre-manufacturing company. In 1890, W. E. Bartlett patented the Clincher tyre, in which the cover was retained on the rim by the pressure of the air in the tube, while in 1892 the Dunlop Company adopted Charles Kingston Welch's wired-on cover and well-base rim, which was patented in 1890 and still in world-wide use in 1974.

During the 1890s, many rival types of pneumatic were put on the market, but it was the Dunlop-Welch tyre which set the pace (although it was the Clincher which found favour with motorists in the 1897–1925 period).

Many men have made fortunes out of the pneumatic tyre, which was a fundamental part of the transportation revolution, but John Boyd Dunlop remained a vet all his life, although he eventually learned how to ride a bicycle. He died on 23 October 1921 in Dublin and his son, the world's first rider on pneumatics, predeceased him by a year.   DBW

WAS THIS AMERICA'S FIRST CAR?

Did the Duryea brothers produce America's first motor car? This has always been a controversial question

WHO BUILT AMERICA'S FIRST CAR? The question has been the subject of controversy almost as long as motor vehicles have existed in the United States, and the number of claimants is legion: Plass, Haynes, Schloemer, Ford, Lambert, King and so on. However, one thing is certain: the first company set up in America to manufacture cars for sale to the public was organised by the Duryea brothers, Charles and Frank. Though the precise details were clouded in later years by Charles's mendaciousness, which led to a quarrel between the two, it seems that Charles was the dreamer and Frank the doer; Charles had the ideas and Frank had to make them work.

Charles, the elder brother, was born in 1861, the son of a farmer in Canton, Illinois; Frank was eight years younger. From an early age, Charles was intrigued by the concept of self-propelled transportation; he built a high-wheel bicycle, using a 42 in wheel from a corn cultivator, a tiny rear wheel from a toy cart and a curved sapling for a frame. In 1882, he graduated from the Giddings Seminary at LeHarpe, Illinois, writing a thesis on 'Rapid Transit', in which he prophesied that a flying machine would eventually be able to cross the Atlantic in half a day. He moved to St Louis, where he entered the cycle trade; he seems to have been a natural wanderer, for he had soon transferred operations to Peoria, Illinois, where, in partnership with a man named Rouse, he built the Sylph, one of the earliest drop-frame ladies' bicycles. From Peoria, Charles went on to Washington DC, then to Rockaway, New Jersey, where Frank, who had just left high school, joined him.

During these peregrinations, Charles had visited the 1886 Ohio State Fair, where a mechanic from Dayton (home town of the Wright Brothers), H. K. Shanck, exhibited a crude internal-combustion engine that he hoped to adapt to drive a tricycle. Duryea became obsessed with the idea of building a gasoline motor wagon and, late in 1891, he visited Frank (by now working as a toolmaker at the Ames Manufacturing Company, of Chicopee Falls, Massachusetts), and told him that he had found the ideal engine and transmission for the proposed motor vehicle. This was a debatable point, for the engine was an untried design by C. E. Hawley, of the Pope cycle company of Hartford, Connecticut, which had a 'free piston' fitting over the normal piston to open and close the exhaust valve, while the friction transmission was of dubious practicality.

Nevertheless, Charles began to look for a backer to finance the building of a car, and a fortuitous meeting in a tobacconist's shop with a businessman named Erwin F. Markham led to Markham offering to advance $1000 towards the cost of a car, in return for a 10 per cent interest in the machine (which would rise to 50 per cent if the backing continued until the car was a success).

Frank agreed to build the car, found a workshop and

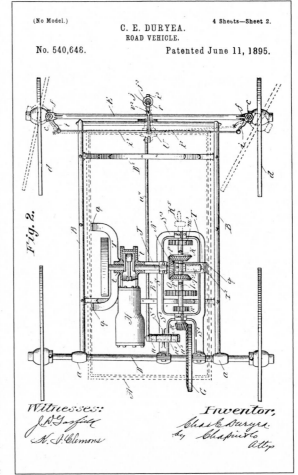

(No Model.) 4 Sheets—Sheet 2.

C. E. DURYEA.
ROAD VEHICLE.

No. 540,648. Patented June 11, 1895.

Fig. 2.

Witnesses:
J. D. Garfield
H. S. Clemons

Inventor:
Charles E. Duryea
by Chapin & Co
Att'y

Above left: the Duryea of 1896 was based on the Benz cars which had captured the imagination of designer Frank Duryea. Thirteen of these cars were built during 1896 and two of them were shipped to Britain to take part in the London–Brighton Emancipation Day rally

Left: a page of the first patent taken out by Charles Duryea. This is dated 11 June 1895. In the bottom right-hand corner of the picture can be seen the signature of Charles Duryea himself. It was this patent that caused great friction between the two Duryea brothers, as the original design had been the work of Frank Duryea and not Charles

bought a second-hand phaeton which he planned to adapt to take the engine and transmission. He began work in April 1892, and continued right through the summer. Meanwhile, Charles, smitten with the old wanderlust, had gone back to Peoria and the Rouse-Duryea Cycle Company, leaving Frank to struggle with the unfinished car. Illness held up the work until January 1893, by which time Markham was understandably demanding to see some progress and threatening to withdraw his backing. Having managed to complete the free-piston engine to Hawley's vague design, Frank now found that it would not run. As a desperation measure, he pinned the pistons together, and made the engine perform well enough for him to extract some more money out of Markham, though it was too clumsy and feeble to fit in the carriage. Duryea then designed and built an entirely new power unit and, by September, the car was ready for the road. The first public trial took place on 22 September 1893; 'But,' recalled Frank in 1948, 'because of its friction transmission, the car was barely operative, and I was never

Above: these two sketches portray the Duryea brothers, Charles (*top*) and Frank (*below*) and were made about 1894, the period during which the two men were struggling to have their experiments in motoring construction accepted

Right: a 1904 Duryea produced by the British Duryea company, which was established in Coventry in 1901. The operation was headed by Henry Sturmey, founder editor of *The Autocar*, but survived only until 1907

able to give a demonstration to a possible investor'.

Once again, Markham threatened to withdraw, but Frank managed to persuade him to provide enough cash to pay for the construction of a proper friction clutch and three-speed gearing (but had to forego a salary); in January 1894, the car made its first successful run. Markham, however, had run out of spare cash —and patience.

In March 1894, Frank, after six weeks without salary, found a new backer, much to brother Charles's annoyance—was not he the family wheeler-dealer?— and began work on a second car. To keep his brother informed, Frank mailed a set of drawings of the new car to Peoria and Charles promptly patented them in his own name, sparking off a dispute that would outlive them both.

Frank, now out on his own, demonstrated the second car throughout the summer and, in September 1895, set up the Duryea Motor Wagon Company at Springfield, Illinois. Two months later, he won the first American motor race, organised by the *Chicago Times-Herald*; 80 cars were entered, only six turned up at the start, and only the Duryea and a Benz finished. For some reason, Frank Duryea was so taken with the design of the Benz that he based his next model on it; 13 of these were built for sale during 1896, and two of them were shipped to Britain to take part in the London–Brighton Emancipation Day Run that November, where they impressed *The Autocar* with their performance: 'The Duryea made but little noise, and was going great guns; indeed, its pace, as it ran off the grade on to the level, could not have been less than twenty miles per hour'.

As the Duryea had not been built by one of motor mogul Harry J. Lawson's companies, there were subsequent attempts to denigrate its showing—claims, even, that it had not actually been driven to Brighton, but had been taken down by train and then splashed with mud—but the facts that the car was involved in a traffic accident at Crawley, where it knocked down a little girl named Dyer, and that its passenger, coach-builder G. H. Thrupp, of Thrupp & Maberley, testified on oath that he had travelled all the way to Brighton, bear out its claim to first place in the heavy car section of the run.

Frank Duryea even set up an import agency near Cannon Street in the City of London, headed by one J. L. McKim.

However, the motor car was still too much of a novelty to be a commercial success—one of the first 13 Duryeas was loaned to Barnum & Bailey's Circus as an added attraction among the clowns, freaks and performing animals of the Greatest Show on Earth— and in 1898 the Duryea Motor Wagon Company folded. Frank tried to carry on alone, built one car, and then joined the Stevens Arms & Tool Company, of Chicopee as Vice-President and Chief Engineer in 1901; he designed the Stevens-Duryea car, which was an immediate success (50 were sold in the first season of production) and became one of America's top quality cars of the Edwardian era. Frank sold out in 1915, when the firm was at the peak of its success. He travelled extensively and, though beset by periodic bouts of ill-health, survived to the age of 97, dying on 15 February 1967.

Charles Duryea picked up the pieces of the Motor Wagon Company, which was reformed in 1898 as the Duryea Power Company, of Waterloo, Iowa, though production does not seem to have got under way properly for a couple of years, except for a number of three-wheelers with rear engines. Four-wheelers were added to the range around 1900. Initially, these had

flat-twin engines, but soon the characteristic power unit of these second-generation Duryeas was evolved. It was a splash-lubricated, 10 hp, transverse-three-cylinder engine, probably the first to employ an offset, crankshaft, which gave a direct thrust on the driving stroke. These cars featured a perfected version of the 'one-hand control' essayed in primitive form on the 1893 car; moving a lever between the seats from side to side steered the car, pulling it back shifted the two-speed epicyclic gear into low speed, twisting the grip opened the throttle, and pushing the lever down engaged neutral.

Claimed Duryea, 'The whole control of the car is effected almost by a thought'. In fact, the steering

probably was the most scientifically laid out of the period.

'Carriages, not machines', was the slogan under which these cars were marketed, and the shell-shaped coachwork had a baroque charm all its own. The Duryea was like no other veteran car, each of which Charles Duryea dismissed as 'a cross between a locomotive and a fire engine'.

In 1901, a British Duryea Company was organised at Coventry, initially as a sales agency for the American-built cars. In 1904, though, production of British-built Duryeas began, using parts manufactured by Willans & Robinson of Rugby. The operation was headed by Henry Sturmey, founder-editor of *The Autocar*, but survived only until 1907.

The American company, which moved to Reading, Pennsylvania in 1903, had persisted with the original Power Carriages during this period, but now went off at a tangent, producing a crude, solid-tyred high-wheeler for 1908, under the name Buggyaut. The twin-cylinder engine drove the rear wheels by friction and, in most respects, the car was inferior to the 1895 model. However, it lasted until 1913 at least, and a curious sports version was illustrated in the *Light Car* as late as 1916. By this time, Charles Duryea had returned to the three-wheeler theme with the Duryea Gem, a torpedo-like cyclecar with Buggyaut engine and transmission. It lasted for only a very short period from 1916 until 1917.

'Follow me and you will have diamonds', Charles Duryea had once said to Frank. But there is no difference in chemical composition between diamonds and charcoal, and all Charles's projects seemed to end in ashes. He died in 1938, aged 76, convinced in his own mind that he had built and operated America's first car in 1891, two years before brother Frank had actually made his first faltering run down Spruce Street, Springfield.   DBW

THE TREND-SETTER OF THE GRAND PRIX SERIES

The Dutch Grand Prix is Holland's premier motor race and is famous for a number of remarkable events which proved to be either unique or trend-setting

THE DUTCH GRAND PRIX is held at Zandvoort and is a trend-setting and often unique event. In 1959, Jo Bonnier won, giving BRM their first-ever World-Championship Grand Prix victory, after nine years of failure. In 1961, every starter finished—without even a pit stop; in 1962, Graham Hill had his first-ever win in a World Championship race; in 1967, the now-famous Ford Grand Prix engine won on its maiden outing; in 1968, Jackie Stewart's victory in a Matra saw the first World Championship win for a French-built car and, from the eighteen occasions the race has been of World Championship status, the race winner has progressed to become the season's World Champion no less than eleven times.

In 1949, the *Grote Prijs van Zandvoort* was run to current Formula One regulations ($1\frac{1}{2}$ litres supercharged or $4\frac{1}{2}$ litres unsupercharged), and this event was retrospectively given the title of the first Dutch Grand Prix. Run in two 25-lap heats and a forty-lap final, the race attracted a strong international entry. Scuderia Ferrari entered two 125s for Luigi Villoresi and his protégé Alberto Ascari. Villoresi won heat one from fellow Italian Giuseppe Farina's Maserati 4CLT/48 while, in heat two, Reg Parnell triumphed in his Maserati 4CLT/48 over Ascari. In the wet final, it was Villoresi by over half-a-minute from Emmanuel de Graffenried's Maserati 4CLT/48, with the similar cars of 'B. Bira' and Farina third and fourth. Ascari retired owing to a sheared stub axle.

The 1950 season witnessed the first year of the new World Championship series, but the first official Dutch Grand Prix was not on the list of qualifying rounds; the race was not granted Championship status until 1952. Nevertheless, with the exception of the all-conquering Alfa Romeo team, a full-scale entry was received. Racing on a drying track after morning rain, Juan Manuel Fangio took his Maserati 4CLT/48 into the lead, ahead of fellow-Argentinian Froilan Gonzalez's similar car and French expert Raymond Sommer's Lago-Talbot, which had proved quickest in practice thanks to a new twelve-plug, 260 bhp engine. Sommer moved into the lead after nine of the ninety laps, but his tyres wilted under the strain and he had to stop for a fresh set of rears. Later, his engine expired with valve trouble and, with Fangio's Maserati also withdrawn with failed dampers, the steady and reliable Louis Rosier, then 45, moved ahead. His unsupercharged Lago-Talbot went through non-stop and beat the supercharged cars, which lost their speed advantage by having to stop for fuel. With Gonzalez delayed by a fire in the pits (quickly extinguished, although Froilan had to change his singed trousers), Luigi Villoresi's single-stage-supercharged works Ferrari 125GP beat team-mate Alberto Ascari's Formula Two model 2-litre Ferrari 166C to second place by a mere 0.6 seconds. The last half of the race was held in pouring rain.

Both Alfa Romeo and Ferrari elected to give the

Below: the flag has just fallen for the start of the 1962 Dutch Grand Prix and Graham Hill's BRM leads Dan Gurney's Porsche and John Surtees' Lola-Climax. Hill went on to win the race and score his first World Championship race victory

Left: a view of the crowded pit front during the practice session prior to the 1971 Dutch Grand Prix. In the background, the clouds are already building up and the race itself was held in pouring rain. Victory went to the brilliant young Belgian Jacky Ickx after a fantastic struggle with Pedro Rodriguez. Jackie Stewart, whose Tyrrell was fitted with unsuitable tyres, finally finished eleventh after being lapped no less than five times

1951 event a miss, leaving nine rather uncompetitive Formula One cars opposing three works Formula Two HWMs from Britain. Giuseppe Farina's ageing Maserati 4CLT/48 screamed into the lead, chased by an assortment of Lago-Talbots led initially by Belgian André Pilette's model. Farina was destined to retire with a broken oil pipe, while Pilette overturned his car and was thrown out, suffering slight head injuries so, for the second year running, Louis Rosier triumphed. Amazingly, twenty-year-old Stirling Moss rocketed round in second place in his underpowered HWM, ahead of cars with more than twice the engine capacity; in the closing stages, however, the HWM's Alta engine began to misfire. Moss stopped at the pits with two laps to go to change a plug, and shot out again minus the engine cover, as third man Philippe Etancelin hove into view. Alas, the misfire was still there, Etancelin took second position and Moss stammered round to claim third.

In 1952, the race was granted World Championship status but, with the current Formula One on the decline, the Dutch opted to hold the race for 2-litre Formula Two cars. True to form, no one could catch Alberto Ascari, whose works Ferrari 500 won six of the seven championship qualifiers that year (he did not start the seventh). Team mates Giuseppe Farina and Luigi Villoresi made it a Ferrari 1-2-3, but in the opening stages the pair had been led by the rising British star, Mike Hawthorn. The 23-year-old Surrey driver handled his underpowered Bristol-engined Cooper with verve, but eventually had to give best to the Ferraris and settled for fourth place, two laps down. Nevertheless, Mike's Cooper soundly trounced the Italian Maseratis and French Gordinis.

The following year's race saw another start-to-finish victory for Ascari, with Farina second. Villoresi's car retired with a broken throttle, while new Ferrari recruit Mike Hawthorn was fourth, behind the first of the now-faster Maseratis. This was the A6SSG model, driven initially by veteran Italian Felice Bonetto, but taken over by the faster Froilan Gonzalez who had broken the rear axle of his own car early in the race.

There was no Dutch Grand Prix in 1954. The circuit was in need of extensive resurfacing, and the Royal Dutch Automobile Club thought it not worthwhile running the race, as the new Mercedes-Benz Grand

Prix cars would not be ready. So the first Dutch Grand Prix under the 2½-litre Formula One was not run until 1955. This was only a week after the world's worst motor-racing accident, when 81 spectators were killed at Le Mans. Whereas other motor races were cancelled, the Dutch thought their circuit well up to safety requirements and went ahead. Throughout the 100 laps, the two Mercedes-Benz W196 cars of Juan Manuel Fangio and Stirling Moss raced nose-to-tail, annihilating the Ferrari, Maserati and Gordini opposition.

Financial problems caused the Grand Prix to be cancelled for two years, so it was Whit Monday 1958 before Formula One cars echoed round the sand dunes of Zandvoort again. Within the intervening three years, British cars had surged to the forefront. Ferrari were the only real opposition, Maserati having retired at the end of 1957, and Mercedes-Benz at the end of 1955. Driving a Vanwall, Stirling Moss led from start to finish and a surprise second and third were the two works BRM P25s of Franco-American Harry Schell and France's Jean Behra. It was BRM's best result in World Championship racing until the 1959 GP, when Jo Bonnier scored the British team's first World-Championship Grand Prix win. With twelve of the 75 laps to go, early leader Stirling Moss had retired when his Cooper's gearbox failed, leaving victory to Bonnier's BRM with the works Coopers of Jack Brabham and Masten Gregory second and third.

By 1960, rear-engined cars had well and truly taken over in Formula One. Only the Ferrari, Aston Martin and American Scarab teams relied on front-engined machinery; in fact, the Aston Martin and the Scarabs were withdrawn after practising, while Ferrari already had an experimental rear-engined machine which appeared in practice. Jack Brabham's works Cooper shot in front, with Stirling Moss in Rob Walker's privately entered Lotus giving chase. Moss was biding his time, knowing he could overtake at any time, when his plans came unstuck on lap seventeen. Brabham's Cooper flicked up a kerbstone which burst a tyre and broke a wheel on Moss's Lotus. Moss spun helplessly at 120 mph, narrowly missing some trees, and lost a lap at the pits having a new wheel fitted. He resumed and, in lap-record-breaking style, climbed up to fourth place only inches behind Graham Hill's BRM P48. Brabham continued to a comfortable victory over Innes Ireland's works Lotus 18. A shadow was cast over the race when Dan Gurney's BRM P48 suffered a rear brake failure going into Tarzan curve after the long straight, and his car sped helplessly into the dunes and turned upside-down. Gurney was unhurt, but some spectators standing in a prohibited area were injured, one fatally.

The 1961 race, run to new 1½-litre Grand Prix regulations, was unique in that all fifteen starters finished, without even a pit stop! As the British teams were largely unprepared for the new formula, Ferrari were left to dominate the race. The German Wolfgang von Trips scored his first-ever Grand Prix win, leading American Phil Hill over the line by 0.9 secs. Third, in his underpowered Climax-engined Lotus 21, was Jim Clark, and fourth was Stirling Moss in Rob Walker's older-model Lotus 18 after a race-long duel with the third Ferrari of American Richie Ginther.

By 1962, however, the British teams had more than caught up. New V8 engines from Coventry Climax (used by Lotus, Cooper and Lola) and BRM were easily the match of Ferrari's V6, and the new flat-8s from Porsche. Jim Clark gave the new monocoque Lotus 25, a machine which set design trends for years to come, its debut and led for eleven laps before the

gearbox failed. Graham Hill took over the lead to score his first-ever Grand Prix win, and pave the way to his first World Championship, also giving BRM a much-needed boost after a 'win or give up' ultimatum from owner Sir Alfred Owen.

The mid 1960s were the era of Jim Clark. As if to underline this, the Scotsman won the Dutch Grand Prix in 1963, 1964 and 1965, at the wheel of a works Lotus. In 1963, he lapped even the second man, while his winning margin the following year was almost a minute. In 1965, however, there were only eight seconds in it. A new threat, also from Scotland, had emerged: Jackie Stewart in a works BRM.

In 1966, for the first year of the 3-litre Formula One, Lotus had a poor year, Clark having to rely for much of the season on his 1965 Lotus 33 fitted with a Climax V8 'stretched' to 2 litres. Despite the handicap of a 2-litre engine instead of a 3-litre as used by most works teams, Clark took, and held, the lead in the Dutch Grand Prix. However, the engine began to lose water and two pit stops for the precious liquid dropped him to third. Winner was the wily Jack Brabham in his 3-litre Repco-engined Brabham BT19. Brabham, on pole position, had made great play of the fact that he was the oldest man in the race by hobbling up to his car on the grid wearing a false beard and leaning on a walking stick!

The following year saw the *début* of the Cosworth-designed Ford DFV Grand Prix engine. It was a victorious *début*, with Jim Clark's Lotus 49 winning comfortably from the works Brabhams of Jack Brabham and Denny Hulme and the Ferrari of Chris Amon, with the rest nowhere. The engine had only fired for the first time two months before, while Clark's Lotus was brand new before practice had started. Clark's team-mate, Graham Hill, in the sister Lotus 49-Ford, had been fastest in practice, and led the opening ten laps before a timing gear broke.

The 1968 race was held in miserable conditions. The rain became worse as the race progressed and so it was all a question of tyres—plus the superior driving of Jackie Stewart, who gave Ken Tyrrell's Matra MS10-Ford its first Grand Prix win. It was also the first World Championship race win for a French-built car and Dunlop's first major victory for two years, following the upsurge of Firestone and Goodyear in 1966. Jean-Pierre Beltoise in the all-French Matra MS11 V12 was second, the Frenchman being the fastest driver on the circuit, thanks to wet-weather Dunlops (Stewart had 'intermediates'), and making up time well after a pit stop to clear sand from his throttle slides.

Once Jochen Rindt's Lotus 49B-Ford had retired with a broken drive-shaft joint, Jackie Stewart's Matra MS80-Ford went on to an easy win in the 1969 race. Jo Siffert's Rob Walker-entered Lotus 49B-Ford was a creditable second, with Chris Amon's Ferrari, Denny Hulme's McLaren and the Brabhams of Jacky Ickx and Jack Brabham in hot pursuit. New four-wheel-drive cars from Matra and Lotus appeared in practice, but were withdrawn for further development.

The 1970 Dutch Grand Prix was clouded with tragedy. Once he had overtaken early leader Jacky Ickx's Ferrari 312B, Jochen Rindt was unbeatable in the Lotus 72-Ford. Second was Jackie Stewart's hard-driven, uncompetitive March 701-Ford and third Ickx, after a meteoric drive following a pit-stop due to a puncture. Just over one-quarter distance, a cloud of black smoke billowed over the far side of the circuit; Piers Courage had inexplicably lost control of his De Tomaso 505-Ford. It hit the bank, overturned and caught fire. Courage was killed instantly.

There was a race in 1971, held in the wet, but the

drivers were upset that few of the safety measures recommended by the CSI of the FIA had been carried out on the circuit. Newspaper reporters concentrated more on the safety angle than the fantastic duel between the world's top two wet-weather drivers, Jacky Ickx and Pedro Rodriguez. Ickx's Ferrari 312B-2/70 eventually triumphed over the Mexican's BRM P160, and the remaining runners were lapped at least once; Jackie Stewart, his Tyrrell-Ford on unsuitable tyres, was 11th, lapped five times.

There was no Dutch Grand Prix in 1972, because the drivers complained, once again, about safety at Zandvoort.

Safety work and track modernisation were completed in time for the Grand Prix in 1973—only just, as the paddock area received its final surfacing the day before practice—and, in the race, Jackie Stewart and François Cevert scored an excellent 1-2 for Tyrrell-Ford after Ronnie Peterson's John Player Special-Ford had failed in the closing laps, with engine and gearbox problems. Sadly, it was a Dutch Grand Prix once more overshadowed by tragedy. The 25-year-old British driver Roger Williamson crashed his March 731-Ford into the guard-rail, which gave way and acted as a launching pad. The March landed upside-down and caught alight. Marshals were hesitant in rescue attempts and it was left to another British driver, David Purley, to try to rescue the almost uninjured Williamson. Attempts to release him were in vain, however, and the flames eventually engulfed the car, killing its driver. Outrage swept the motor-racing world: £350,000 had been spent on updating the circuit yet the human element was at fault—no one had trained the marshals to deal with an emergency. MK

Top: Ronnie Peterson's Lotus 72-Ford leads Jackie Stewart's Tyrrell at the start of the 1973 race. Sadly, the young British driver Roger Williamson crashed his March during the race and was killed

Above: Jackie Stewart's Tyrrell-Ford rounds a bend during the 1971 Grand Prix. Stewart had a miserable race, but made up for it in 1973 when he and Tyrrell team-mate Francois Cevert scored a dramatic 1–2 triumph

A POPULAR GENERATOR FOR THE CAR

Most cars require electricity for their ignition as well as for their ancillary equipment.
The dynamo is effective and popular as a provider of the necessary energy

A cutaway view of a dynamo as used on a car. In this type of unit, the armature consists of a large number of coils, each connected to the commutator. The greater the number of coils, the smoother the output of the dynamo; unfortunately, however, the mass of the armature has to be great and too high an operating speed can lead to the component's explosion. Note that there is a roller bearing at the front *(left)*, where the unit is driven, and a plain bearing at the relatively unstressed rear *(right)*, where, on the unit shown in this example, tachometer drive is provided

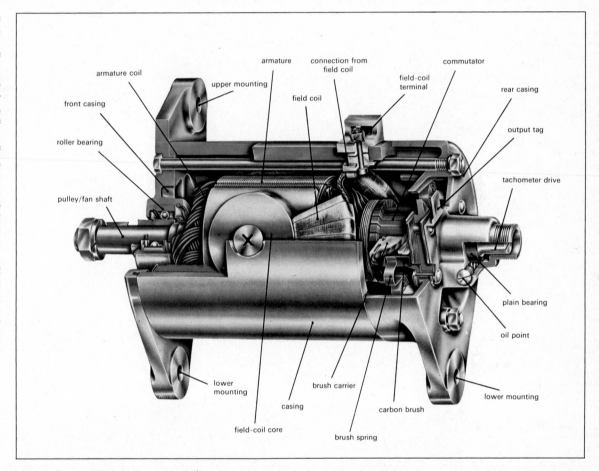

UNLESS A MOTOR VEHICLE has a diesel engine, it is bound to consume electricity, because ignition is brought about by an electrical spark. A battery can provide this current, without any trouble, but it will eventually run flat if it not recharged by a generator, be this an alternator or a dynamo.

Most cars built since the early 1970s have had alternators, because these are more reliable and more efficient than the older dynamos. Previous to this time, however, dynamos were standard items on motor cars, producing sufficient electricity to power not only the engine ignition system, but also the lights, windscreen wipers, heater fan etc.

Since the early part of the twentieth century, electric starter motors have been fitted to cars, thus dispensing with the need to 'swing the handle'. These motors demand enormous current supplies, which would soon discharge the battery if it were not for the generator.

In just about every road-going car, the dynamo is driven by a rubber belt from the end of the crankshaft. By varying the relative sizes of the crankshaft and dynamo pulleys, it is possible, too, to alter the relative speeds of the two items. Before considering this,

however, we should discuss how a dynamo works.

If a coil of wire is rotated within a magnetic field, an electric current will be generated in that coil. The size of the current will depend on the speed of rotation and the strength of the magnetic field. If the current is taken direct from each end of the coil, through two slip rings and brushes, it will alternate, changing direction twice for every revolution of the coil. The best way of avoiding this alternation, which is no good for charging a battery, is to fit a commutator, which is in the form of a single slip ring split into two parts, so that when the current changes direction it is fed into the wiring system 'the other way round'.

In practice, the dynamo has more than one coil—usually 28, in fact—with 28 segments on the commutator (there is no need for 56 segments, because two coils can share two segments between their four wires). The result of having a large number of coils is that any ripples in the current output, caused by the change in current direction, will be all but smoothed out.

The electrical output is taken from the commutator by means of two carbon brushes. These make contact with the commutator as it turns with the armature—the

581

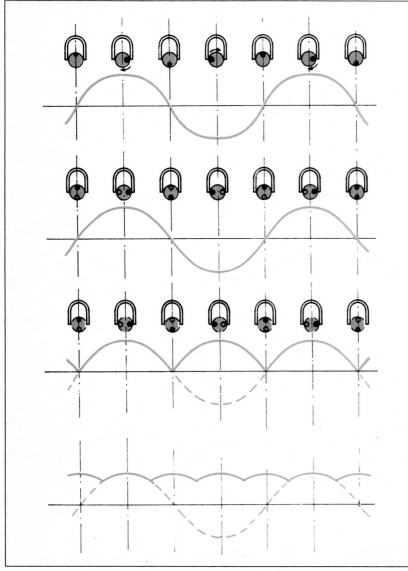

name given to the coil assembly—and transmit current to the regulator, which controls the voltage and current output, and thence to the battery.

If the dynamo were allowed to produce its full output at all times, it would use engine power unnecessarily, because the higher the output, the harder the unit is to turn. To overcome this, the permanent magnets used to produce the field, in which the armature spins, are replaced by further coils of wire, known as the field coils. When these coils are energised, an equivalent magnetic field is produced, but the beauty of the arrangement is that if the field-coil supply is cut down, the dynamo output will be reduced accordingly.

The supply to the field coil is controlled by the regulator, which is sensitive to dynamo/battery voltage and to the charging current. In other words, the dynamo should only give its full output when the battery is not fully charged or when large demands are being made.

Although the dynamo is a reliable and fairly efficient piece of equipment, it has certain drawbacks when compared with the more modern alternator. The main one is that it will not produce sufficient current to charge a battery if it is rotating at less than about 1200 rpm (or at tickover). Unfortunately, it is no use fitting a smaller dynamo pulley to overcome this, as the maximum safe speed of this type of generator is around 7000 rpm (it has been known for the armature to explode when over-revved). The alternator is safe to around 12,000 rpm, so it can be higher geared.

The maximum output available from a modern dynamo is around 22 amps, which is sufficient for most uses, but which can be too little when driving on a wet night with the heater fan on as well as the headlights and windscreen wipers. An alternator can produce up to 50 amps, although the figure is usually more like 40.

The only maintenance necessary is an occasional drop of oil, on the rear bearing. The most important point is to keep the drive belt at the correct tension—with half an inch of play in its longest section; it may take half a horsepower to drive the dynamo when the battery charge is low and a loose fan belt will start to slip under these conditions, allowing the battery to become further discharged.   IW

Above: these diagrams illustrate the basic principle of the generator. They represent, graphically, the current produced by coils turning in the field of a horseshoe magnet. In the top two cases, an alternating current is produced by single and double coils, respectively, half being positive and half negative, with respect to zero. The third diagram shows two coils, but with the current collected by a commutator, thereby producing a pulsing direct current. The last diagram shows the output from a four-coil dynamo

Right: a dynamo on a Vauxhall 1500 cc engine

MEASURING THE POWER

POWER IS DEFINED AS the rate of doing work. A James Watt horse (which is weaker, but more consistent, than the natural variety) can do 33,000 lb ft (4550 kg m) of work in one minute—for example, by raising a 330 lb weight through 100 ft. The torque developed by an engine is expressed in the same units of the pound and the foot (or their metric or other equivalents), which give us a measure of the work the engine is doing; if this be related to time by introducing the rate of crankshaft rotation in revolutions per minute, the power of the engine (its rate of doing work, remember) may be calculated.

The machine used for measuring this torque, and hence the power, is called a dynamometer. It simply applies a measurable load to the engine; measurement of the load gives a direct value for the torque, and if, at the same time, the crankshaft rate be measured by a tachometer (alternatively called a revolution counter), the two figures may be related mathematically to produce a value for power. Even when, as is sometimes the case, a power meter gives direct instrumental reading of power on a dynamometer installation, the actual measurement of power is still indirect: voltage from an electrical torque meter and current from an electrical tachometer are fed into a wattmeter which is calibrated in brake horsepower.

Why 'brake'? Because the power measured is what the engine delivers 'on the brake'—that is, against the load applied by the dynamometer. The best known forms of engine test stands incorporate an hydraulic dynamometer, or water brake, in which a paddlewheel, driven by the engine, rotates inside a casing that has internal vanes and is filled with water. The churning of the water absorbs the engine's power, and the torque reaction transmitted by the water to the casing makes it tend to rotate in the same direction as the drive shaft. Simple measurement of the force necessary to restrain the casing and prevent such movement provides a measure of the torque developed by the engine. The restraining force is usually applied to an arm projecting radially from the casing; in the older and cruder machines, weights were hung on the arm, but later it became the practice to apply a spring balance or, later still, an electrical strain-gauge.

A popular alternative to the water brake is the electrical dynamometer. This is, in effect, a large dynamo driven by the engine, and the current generated when it is turned may be fed into the factory electrical system or put to good use in some other way. The advantage of the electrical dynamometer is that it can be switched to act as an electric motor: when used to drive the engine on the test bed, the power required to do this (the process is known as 'motoring' the engine) can be measured. Accurate information about the frictional losses within the engine can thus be obtained, and the mechanical efficiency calculated. Adding the brake horsepower and the friction horsepower together gives a figure known as the indicated horsepower, which is a measure of the power actually developed inside the cylinders.

All these techniques are suitable for employment in a factory or tuning establishment where it is possible and convenient to work on bare engines. Often it is desirable to be able to make power measurements while the engine is still in the car and, for this, a 'rolling-road' or chassis dynamometer is used. The car is held with its driving wheels resting upon a pair of large-diameter rollers, the greater parts of which are beneath the floor. The car engine is started, the gears and clutch engaged just as if driving normally, and the tyres drive the rollers round. One of the rollers will be connected to some form of dynamometer which,

in this case, will measure the power that actually reaches the road after some has been lost in the transmission and tyres. This is the most realistic form of power measurement, and it allows quite accurate inferences of vehicle performance to be made. On the other hand, the inefficiency of the transmission can mask the true condition and performance of the engine.

Nevertheless, the chassis dynamometer plays a useful part in some of the most particular scientific work which is performed on cars. For instance, a car may be 'driven' on it through a representative pattern of accelerations, gearchanges, cruising and idling, while the exhaust gases are collected and analysed for noxious constituents. The car's contribution to atmospheric pollution in urban traffic may thus be forecast. Exhaust analysis may also be carried out in conjunction with test-stand dynamometers: in this case, the information is likely to be used for establishing ignition and fuel-mixture settings. In fact, the test stand or engine dynamometer is a scientific instrument capable of much valuable work in investigating lubrication, fatigue, cooling, combustion and every other aspect of an engine's behaviour. It may even be installed in a climatically controlled chamber for cold-weather or high-altitude tests to be simulated, for example.

The chassis dynamometer has its own ways of being inaccurate. The power losses in the tyres are slightly greater than they would be on the road, for the deflections they suffer on the rollers are different from those that are normal. In many installations, the tachometer is driven from one of the rollers while the dynamometer is driven from the other; again, because of the tyres' different reactions to each roller, discrepancies may be introduced.　LJKS

Above: a front-wheel-drive Fiat 127 being tested on a dynamometer. As can be seen from the picture, there is more to it than just starting the car and running it for an indefinite period. First, the car's exhaust must be carried by pipes out of the building lest the workshop fill with intoxicating fumes. Also, a large fan feeds the radiator with cool air, something which would be done by the air-stream were the car on the road

The world's toughest rally

Held over 4000 miles of the world's most diabolical roads, in totally unpredictable weather, the Safari has become recognised as the most difficult rally of them all

WHEN THE GREAT EUROPEAN RALLIES, like the Liège-Rome-Liège, the Monte Carlo and the Alpine, were in their heyday, few European rally drivers had heard of the Safari, let alone thought about taking part in it. As tourism increased, public opinion began to swing against the classic road rallies of the 1950s and 1960s, so they were either abandoned or watered down into long mileages of boring main-road driving, interspersed with short special stages on closed roads

or private land. The big European rallies had been little more than thinly disguised road races for production cars and, as they lost their bite, so manufacturers began to lose interest in them, for they knew only too well that the public who read about rallies were quite aware that they were no longer the great test of a motor car that they had once been. In consequence, the big car makers became more selective in the events they chose to enter, and turned to events in countries where the publicity resulting from victory would assist car sales. So the trend shifted away from Europe to a certain extent, and European manufacturers began to enter rallies in Canada, Australia and Africa, as well as the well publicised events like the London to Sydney Marathon and the World Cup Rally.

One such event which gained rapidly in stature was the East African Safari, for the huge mileages and appalling roads of the rally provided the competitors with one of the stiffest tests that a car can undertake. As a bonus for the winning manufacturer, the enormous publicity gained throughout Africa, and indeed many other continents, bore fruit in the increased car sales which almost inevitably resulted after a victory. The inhabitants of East Africa reckoned that if a car, driven at racing speeds, could survive 4000 miles on the cart tracks which pass for roads in many parts of the continent, then it would survive several years of less hectic driving without falling to bits.

The rally began life in Kenya where a group of British motoring enthusiasts, bored with the total lack of competition motoring, began organising local rallies around Nairobi. In 1953, a small group, led by Eric Cecil, decided to organise a more ambitious event to commemorate the Coronation of Queen Elizabeth II, and so the event was named the Coronation Safari. The lack of special competition cars in Kenya more or less forced the organisers to limit the entries to standard

production cars, and the classes were arranged by the then novel method of price categories. The first event had starting points in Tanzania and Uganda, as well as Kenya, and the rough roads took their toll of the 42 starters, but, at the end of the event, the car with the least penalties was a Volkswagen Beetle driven by Alan Dix, who later became Managing Director of Volkswagen of Great Britain. There was no overall winner of the first event, only class winners, but for the second event it was decided to make the overall winner the car with the least penalty points, irrespective of class.

Unlike the first event, which had been little more than a disguised road race, it was decided to tone down the speed aspect for the 1954 rally, with the result that the event became too easy. However, the organisers were learning the whole time and, before long, the rally took the shape that it still retains today. Many drivers became famous throughout Africa because of their exploits in the Safari, yet for some of them it was the only event in which they took part in the whole year. One early name to emerge was that of Vic Preston who won the 1954 rally in a VW, then switched to a Ford Zephyr to win the 1955 event; although he competed in almost every Safari until the early 1970s, he never won again, but he became the Ford importer for Kenya, and now his son, Vic Preston Junior, is a leading Safari competitor.

The rally had attracted little attention in Europe, but in 1956 Belgian driver Maurice Gatsonides went out to drive a Standard Vanguard and, although he did not distinguish himself, he reported favourably to the sport's organising body, the FIA, and they authorised an international permit for the 1957 event. The rally was switched to coincide with the Easter holiday in 1957, as most of the local competitors had normal full time jobs and they often found difficulty in getting

Opposite page: this could only be Africa, with its untamed, wide-open spaces and untarred roads. Most of the 4000 miles of the Safari are held on roads similar to these

Opposite page, inset: another typical African scene. Here, French drivers Neyret and Terramorsi speed through an African village during the 1965 event

Above left: Mike Armstrong and Walter Young in action in their Ford Zodiac during the 1966 East African Safari

Above: a press photographer stands ready as Jim Cardwell loses his Datsun on a road made treacherous by rain—a common occurrence in East Africa

time off from work, so the four-day Easter holiday seemed the ideal time to run the rally. This brought additional difficulties for competitors, as Easter usually coincides with the short but tempestuous rainy season in East Africa; in these conditions, the dry, dusty red 'murram' roads can be turned from a high speed, if bumpy, track into a quagmire several feet deep in a matter of moments as the torrential rain arrives.

The rain caused tremendous difficulties in 1957: competitors sometimes spent hours stuck in a bad patch of mud, and it was a VW Beetle, with the better traction of its rear-mounted engine, which struggled through to victory. By now, car importers and local dealers were realising the sale potential of a Safari victory, and a measure of professionalism began to creep in. In the early days, this was no more than the loan of spare parts, but this soon escalated into full-scale preparation of special cars, while the top drivers were wooed by offers of payment.

This tended to remove some of the amateur friendliness from the rally, as victory now became extremely important for many people. The shape of squabbles to come was seen in 1958 when the rally ended in protest and counter protest, tribunals, appeals and, finally, a decision by the RAC stewards in London nearly nine months after the rally had finished!

Several foreign drivers entered the 1958 event and in 1959 the first serious European entries came from Ford and Rootes. The Hillman Huskys of the Rootes team did not last long, but the big Ford Zephyrs went well, and Ford chalked up second and third places overall behind the winning Mercedes of Bill Fritschy —another Safari legend who was to win the event in 1960 as well.

For 1960, the event was renamed the East African Safari, since it seemed pointless to carry on celebrating the Coronation some seven years after the event! Other changes included the addition of classes for modified cars and GT cars, while the price categories were abandoned in favour of the same capacity classes used on other major rallies. Rootes, Ford and BMC tackled the 1960 event; the Sunbeam Rapiers and Minis did not last long, but the big Ford Zephyrs won the team prize, with Vic Preston finishing third overall, behind a Mercedes and a Citroën.

Below: Shekhar Mehta, an Asian exiled from Uganda, won the 1973 Safari in a Datsun 240Z. Here he and co-driver Lofty Drews get a wave from a couple of locals

The Mercedes hat-trick was completed in 1961 when John Manussis, the colourful Greek who lived locally, beat Fritschy into second place in a 220SE Mercedes. The Europeans were getting better all the time, though, and the locals were staggered when a' leading British woman driver, Anne Hall, brought her works Ford Anglia into third place. The Ford Zephyrs again won the team prize.

By 1962, the Safari had achieved international fame as the word spread among European drivers of the incredible difficulties of the rally. Nearly a third of the 104 entries in the 1962 event were foreign-entered, and there were teams from Ford, Saab, Rover and Ford Australia. The overseas visitors were decimated in the wickedly muddy conditions, but Erik Carlsson and Pat Moss in their Saabs put up a fine show, with Carlsson leading towards the end, only to have rear suspension failure, while Pat Moss got through into third place behind a VW and a Peugeot.

The legends began to grow around the Safari as overseas drivers brought back stories of incredible adventures, no doubt exaggerating the size of the animals they had hit and the swollen rivers they had been obliged to ford. The foreign factory teams began to spend small fortunes on the event, sending out their crews with practice cars many weeks before the rally, and placing teams of mechanics around the route to repair broken-down cars. However, the organisers prevented changes of major components like engines, gearboxes and axles by painting the components with a special radioactive paint: if the paint was missing when the car reached the finish, it was excluded from the rally. The native population, who relished the excitement of the rally, were able to make a good deal of money by waiting at particularly treacherous spots, and offering to push cars out of the mud for a fee.

Above: in 1972, an all-out attack on the Safari was made by Ford, and victory went to the Escort RS1600 driven by the Finnish Mikkola/ Palm crew. In 1973, however, Ford were forced to concede victory to Datsun

Left: the crew of a Triumph 2000 checking in to a control during the 1974 event

They even built their own hazards for the cars by digging ditches and piling up rocks, then charged the drivers for removing the obstacles!

By 1963, the big cars like the Mercedes and Zephyrs were losing ground to medium sized cars which seemed ideally suited to the terrain; the Peugeot 404, Volvos and Ford Cortinas began to dominate the event, the Peugeot taking the lion's share of the honours, building up a reputation for reliability which no other car, by 1974, had yet matched in Africa. Incredibly, this was achieved with very little assistance from the Peugeot factory which left any preparation work to the local importers. In the six rallies between 1963 and 1968, Peugeot won four times, the team of Nowicki/Cliff winning in 1963 and 1968 and the Shankland/Rothwell team winning in 1966 and 1967.

In 1963, only seven of the 84 starters were classified as finishers, but, instead of putting people off, this brought the works teams back in force the next year, with teams from Volvo, Saab, Ford, Datsun and America's Mercury. Peter Hughes won the rally in a Cortina, and Ford won the team prize, but Hughes was a Kenyan and the legend began to grow that no foreign driver would ever win the rally. They had led by enormous margins at times, but always some mishap seemed to put them out. The local drivers claimed that their year-round experience of the rally roads was invaluable, and that the foreign drivers could not pace themselves, going too fast too soon.

Another legend was born in 1965, when the Sikh, Joginder Singh, partnered by his brother Jaswant, won the rally in a Volvo. Joginder became a popular figure in the rallying world, partly because of the publicity value of having an Asian driver, and he came to Europe to take part in a number of rallies.

The 1966 event saw Derek Gates take over as Clerk of the Course, a job which is combined with almost all the detailed organisational work on the event. The rally changed little in format over the years that followed, except that in 1968 the class system was dropped, as the rugged Safari did not favour any particular size of car or engine while, in 1969, full Group Two rally cars were admitted to the rally for the first time. The ugly face of politics, which had threatened the rally once or twice before, finally emerged when Tanzania refused to let the rally pass through her territory or allow Tanzanian residents to enter, which prevented potential winner Bert Shankland from taking part. However, a first-class route through Kenya and Uganda was devised, and local driver Robin Hill won in a German Ford Taunus. Politics intervened again in 1970 when the Ugandan Government demanded that the rally should start and finish in the country's capital, Kampala. The Kenyans complied with the request as the rally would otherwise have lost much of its flavour, since Tanzania was still barred to the rally.

The Japanese Datsun team had been making an all-out assault on the rally for several years and, in 1970, their persistance was rewarded with victory for a Datsun 1600SSS driven by local man Edgar Herrmann, who returned the following year and won again in a Datsun 240Z. Tanzania had relented, and allowed the rally to run through the country once more, so a more varied route was laid on.

For 1972, the Tanzanians put more pressure on the Kenyans and persuaded them to have the start in Dar-es-Salaam, a change that brought about severe organisational difficulties. Ford of Britain launched an all out attack on the rally, spending £50,000 on long reconnaissance trips, hiring an aircraft, fitting the rally cars with ground-to-air radio, placing teams of

mechanics around the route and covering every eventuality; their Escort RS1600s were driven by Timo Makinen/Henry Liddon, Hannu Mikkola/Gunnar Palm, Vic Preston Jnr./Bev Smith, Joginder Singh/Sembi and Robin Hillyar/Mark Birley. Despite a number of problems, the powerful 200 bhp Escorts proved too much for the Datsuns, and the Mikkola/Palm team became the first foreign drivers to win the rally, while other Ford works cars took third, fourth and eighth places.

The political troubles in Uganda prevented the rally from passing through that territory in 1973, but the rally went on as usual and, despite a strong challenge from Britain's Roger Clark in a works Ford, it was an exiled Ugandan, Shekhar Mehta, in a Datsun 240Z who just beat another Datsun, an 1800SSS driven by Harry Kallstrom.

Tremendous rainfall hindered competitors in the 1974 event, which was held entirely in Kenya because of continuing political troubles, and local experience showed through again when Joginder Singh and David Doig got their Mitsubishi Colt to the finish well clear of their pursuers. Only sixteen of the 99 starters were classified as finishers, due largely to the rainfall; in some places the rain which fell during a period of three or four days was equal to Britain's entire annual rainfall.

With other international rallies falling by the wayside, it seems unlikely that the Kenyans will ever allow the unique Safari Rally to suffer the same fate, for it has a pioneering atmosphere which no other rally can equal.   MT

Above: the East African Safari is recognised as the world's toughest rally and it is not hard to see why. For over 4000 miles, competitors must face the challenge of roads often made dangerous and difficult by heavy rain. Obstacles include wild animals, hostile natives, unpredictable weather and some of the toughest and unforgiving terrain in the world

Progenitor of the six-cylinder engine

THE SIX-CYLINDER ENGINE has become such a common-place item of motor engineering, that it is difficult to realise that when it was introduced, in the 1900s, it was an object of controversy as intense as that which, during the early 1970s, raged over the rotary engine. A concept so revolutionary needed promotion if it was to become a commercial success, and the lasting fame of the six-cylinder power unit can be directly attributed to the man who virtually founded the motoring-public-relations business —Selwyn Francis Edge. He launched the Napier six in 1903.

In 1907, at the height of Edge's fame, one of his friends wrote: 'Mr S. F. Edge has shown a rare and almost unique combination of the abilities, mental and physical, and of the spirit of enterprise tempered by prudence, which is exactly calculated to carry a man to the highest place in connection with the automobile movement'.

However, the irresistible rise of Selwyn Edge began, it seems, almost by chance. Edge was born in the little Australian township of Concord, near Sydney, in 1868, and was taken to England at the age of three. As a young man, he became an enthusiastic cyclist, and held a number of long-distance records on solid-tyred ordinary bicycles and tandem bicycles.

Like many racing cyclists of the day, Edge was an early advocate of the new Dunlop pneumatic tyre, an interest which culminated in his joining the Pneumatic Tyre Company as manager of its London depot.

It was during this period that Edge travelled, in 1895, to Paris, where his friend and fellow racing cyclist, Fernand Charron, gave him his first ride in a motor car—a Panhard & Levassor. A couple of years later, Edge acquired his own car, a similar Panhard, which had finished second in the 1896 Paris–Marseilles race with René de Knyff at the tiller, and which had been brought to England for the Emancipation Day run of 14 November 1896. He ran this for a year or so, and then, as several of its design features were becoming somewhat *passè*, decided to have it updated by his friend Montagu Napier, another former cyclist, who had an old-established engineering works at Lambeth. Napier modified the car extensively, and eventually decided—or was cajoled by Edge—to become a motor manufacturer.

Edge, backed by Harvey du Cros, formed the Motor Power Company in 1899, selling the imported Gladiator and Clément-Panhard cars built by Adolphe Clément, who also controlled the French Dunlop company (as Harvey du Cros owned the British Dunlop company, the tie-up was perhaps inevitable); the Motor Power organisation became the exclusive sales agency for the new Napier cars, and Edge entered the prototype for the 1900 Thousand Miles Trial.

At the turn of the century, no British manufacturer was active in racing, and Edge, fully aware of the publicity to be gained for a car which could successfully challenge the world's best, entered a four-cylinder, 16 hp car for the 1900 Paris–Toulouse–Paris race (his riding mechanic was the Hon C. S. Rolls), only to be eliminated by minor troubles. The following year, Napier built him a monstrous 17-litre racer for the Gordon Bennett Trophy, but its Dunlop tyres could not stand up to the strains of racing and, once more,

Edge was out of the running. In 1902, however, Edge won the Gordon Bennett with a new 40 hp Napier—a hollow victory if ever there was one, for the car upheld the marque's competition record for breakdowns, only winning because the opposition's breakdowns were more serious and caused them all to retire.

He failed to retain the cup the following year for, in the Irish Gordon Bennett, the Napiers ran —or rather, did not run—true to form, and Edge finished last, but was promptly disqualified anyway.

This was his last serious appearance in major open competition—henceforth he acted only as *eminence grise* of the Napier team, and he controlled the sales of its touring cars, which were enjoying a far greater success than the racers. Not that there was anything *gris* about Edge's personality—with his piercing gaze, bristling eyebrows and bushy moustache, he was a striking figure, and one who made enemies as easily as he made friends. His prolific correspondence to the motoring papers was very much a feature of the Edwardian motoring scene.

Of course, he had to fight hard to defend the validity of the six-cylinder concept, which he launched at a dinner at London's Trocadero Restaurant in October 1903—in later years, he recalled the 'courage' of Mr W. Bramson, who bought the first six-cylinder car. Sometimes his arguments were spurious, but they commanded attention.

The Napier was well established as a high-powered luxury car when Edge took the wheel of a racing 60 hp, inaugurating the Brooklands circuit in 1907 with a fantastic solo 24-hour run at an average of 66 mph (fifteen years later he comfortably beat this average with a six-cylinder

Above: S. F. Edge standing behind the driver of a 1921 AC 2-litre at Brooklands, with the Member's Bridge beyond

Spyker, which recorded 74.27 mph over two twelve-hour stints). Under his management, Napier dominated the first two years' racing at Brooklands, then, after his 1908 Grand Prix cars had been debarred from entering the French GP on the grounds that their detachable wire wheels constituted an unfair advantage, Napier withdrew from racing altogether.

In 1912, Edge and Montague Napier quarrelled over marketing policy, and parted company; Edge received £120,000, on condition that he kept out of the motor industry for seven years (which, in view of the intervening World War I, was probably fortuitous), and set up a pig-breeding establishment. Napier, one feels, lost more by the parting than did Edge.

During the war, Edge combined his interests, for he was appointed Controller of Agricultural Machinery to the Ministry of Munitions, and in 1917 the author's great-uncle, Norman Stone, demonstrated the first Fordson tractor to him, which resulted in massive MoM orders for this machine.

In 1921, Edge re-entered the motor industry, acquiring large share-holdings in AC and Cubitt cars, but neither venture prospered and in 1929, when AC collapsed, he retired from the scene.

He published an autobiography in the mid 1930s and inaugurated the Brooklands Campbell Circuit with a 1903 Gordon Bennett Napier in 1937. He died in 1940, when most motorists had quite forgotten this man who was once famed for his courage, physical strength and electrically rapid decision. DBW

THE MOST FAMOUS FLOP OF ALL TIME?

After much research and planning, the Edsel, launched amidst a blaze of publicity, proved to be one of the most famous company disasters ever

THE YEAR 1953 WAS A MOMENTOUS ONE for the Ford Motor Company, which celebrated its fiftieth birthday on 16 June. With the end of the Korean War, sales had taken an upswing, and the company could begin to think about implementing the expansionist policies which had been proposed by Henry Ford II a couple of years earlier.

Aiming at a range which would be fully competitive

with the General Motors line-up, Mr Ford had tentatively forecast that a suitable programme 'might require the introduction of another car name, a new dealer organisation and an additional car division', and had appointed John R. Davis (who had helped the late Edsel Ford create the company's Mercury Division in 1939) to head a committee to look into the viability of such a project.

'Yes,' the Davis Committee reported, 'there *is* a gap in our range. We need a model to compete with the higher-priced Buicks and Oldsmobiles. But there is no need for a new model name or dealer network—call it a Mercury or a Mercury-Monterey—for this would involve unnecessary marketing risks, as General Motors have found to their cost in the past.'

Their findings were backed up by R. J. Eggert, head of Ford's Consumer Research Department: 'As the general standard of living has increased, the consumer has tended to purchase a better car', he reported to the company's executive committee. 'To the average American our present car and its size represent an outward symbol of prestige and well-being.'

The successful launch of the Thunderbird 'personal car' in 1954 gave added strength to demands for a new up-market model and, on 18 May the same year, the

Lincoln-Mercury Division put *their* findings before the Executive Committee.

They thought that the new car should use a Lincoln body-shell on a Mercury chassis, and should sell in the price bracket immediately above the Mercury. For 'identification purposes', they referred to the model as 'the Edsel' (the name of Henry Ford II's father).

Everyone present, it seems, agreed, and the decision to proceed with the new model was taken, though no-one, apparently, gave Robert S. McNamara, newly appointed Assistant General Manager of the Ford Division, a clear answer when he queried: 'What is the new car intended to offer the car-buying public?'

In that heady sellers' market, with Ford missing the first place in US new car sales by only 9000 units in 1954, it seemed that the Lincoln-Mercury formula met every requirement. 'Today's average buyer,' commented *Automobile Topics*, 'clearly wants, and is willing to pay for, that "something extra" that will set his car apart'.

Ford sales figures supported this opinion. McNamara's immediate boss, Lewis Crusoe, had

Top: the first Edsel models were unveiled in 1957. There were two price levels for the new car, with a choice of two power units. Pictured above is the costlier Corsair model, which was fitted with a 410 cu in engine and was offered only with push-button automatic transmission

Above left: the unusual front-end styling of the Edsel

Above: offered with the 361 cu in V8 motor, this is the cheaper of the two models—the Ranger

found that the most basic Ford model, the Mainline, was practically non-saleable.

Enter now F. C. Reith, wearing in his buttonhole the ribbon of the *Legion d'Honneur* (awarded him by an admiring French government for his attempts to place the foundering Ford-France SA factory, at Poissy, on a profitable basis), freshly returned to Dearborn, and appointed to the Ford Product Planning Committee.

He had already proposed certain changes to the design of the 1957 Mercury range which the Committee had approved and now he was dealing with the projected E (for Edsel) Car. On 15 April 1955, he presented his findings for a better-balanced car range, with two E Cars—a low-priced model, and a high-priced model—bracketing the middle-range Mercury. The cheaper E Car was a rival for Dodge and Pontiac, while the more expensive one rivalled Buick, De Soto and Oldsmobile.

The board of directors was agreed: the E car was essential to the success of the company. R. E. Krafve, formerly Assistant General Manager of the Lincoln-Mercury Division, headed the Special Products

Division set up to develop the E Car.

Between conception and realisation of the new car, a time-lag had to be allowed for research, development and tooling; marketing policies, too, were firmly shaped. An added feature during the E Car's two-year gestation period was the search for an identity for the new model: Ford hired the poetess Marianne Moore to dream up possible names for the vehicle. However, the fair versifier's titles drew a blank, and the company returned to the original patronymic—'Edsel'.

A new dealer network was organised, and a publicity and advertising campaign set in motion. In September 1957, the new model was unveiled amid vast publicity. Its styling was, perhaps, over-fussy—certainly the front end, with its curious 'horse collar' radiator grille, heavy bumpers and quadruple headlamps, aroused a lot of discussion, and not a little sales resistance, while the wrap-round windscreen and heavily sculptured tail-fins were reflections of current styling trends.

Beneath the debatable attractions of its exterior, however, the Edsel offered a worthwhile package of engineering innovation—self-adjusting brakes, safety-rim wheels and a new luxury automatic transmission, controlled by push-buttons on the steering-wheel spokes—allied to such proven features as coil-and-

wishbone independent front suspension. There were, as Reith had proposed, two price levels for the new car, with a choice of two power units: both V8s, with swept volumes of 361 and 410 cu in respectively. The cheaper range, consisting of Ranger and Pacer series Edsels, was available with a choice of manual, overdrive or automatic transmissions, but the costlier Corsair and Citation models only had the automatic.

Something, however, had gone wrong, and the market gaps the two ranges were intended to fill no longer existed. In the few months since the project had been initiated, the entire picture of car-sale trends had changed, and the euphoric period of boom had

been succeeded by a mild depression, one in which the rapid growth of the post-Korean War years had given way to a more restrained expansion, and one in which the lower-priced automobile was once more playing a major role—at the expense of that carefully researched 'something extra' car.

In this restricted market, the Edsel collided head-on with the Mercury—and the older marque won. Only 35,000 Edsels were sold during the first six months and the bold sales campaign dwindled away.

Discouragement, it seems, set in too easily, perhaps as a result of the newness of the division controlling the fortunes of the Edsel. Had the campaign been redoubled, the marque might have established itself successfully. As it was, an attempt to widen the Edsel market with a low-cost, in-line, 223 cu in, straight-six engine came too late, and only weeks after the restyled 1960 models had been introduced in November 1959, the Edsel Division ceased operation.

It had been a costly demonstration of the fickleness of the car-buying public; estimates of the amount lost on the Edsel project vary between $250 million and $350 million, but it was a sum which the otherwise successful Ford Motor Company could take in its stride with hardly a falter. And, indeed, when that curious period, when the press claimed that 'Detroit is flying by the seat of its pants', had passed, the fundamental soundness of the new marketing policy was amply proven by the fact that the Company was offering an eight-car line-up in 1963 that covered the market—and sold profitably.

The joker in the pack that trumped the Edsel had been the compact car, represented in the 1960 line-up by the new Falcon and Comet models; when the Edsel was planned, compacts represented only one-twenty-fifth of US car sales—four years later, they had a third of the market. Yet the models which filled that supposedly non-existent gap left by the Edsel also sold well. So was it the time or the car that was wrong? We shall never really be sure.   DBW

Above: the Edsel was launched with a great splash of publicity. This is an advertisement showing the front and rear-end styling of the Edsel

Left: also a feature of Edsel advertising was their claim that the model could be personalised to suit the owner. This is the 'dream interior' on offer to potential Edsel owners

AN ALTERNATIVE POWER SOURCE?

In modern times, much has been written about the feasibility of the electric car.
This type of vehicle, however, has been around for a long time

LIKE A KIND OF AUTOMOTIVE PETER PAN, the electric car emerged early—around the turn of the century, in fact—but has remained at the same stage of development ever since.

The electric car is, indeed, older than the petrol car. In the *Edinburgh Evening Journal* of 17 June 1842 is a report of a clumsy vehicle which appeared on the streets of that city, driven by eight electro-magnets operated by primitive jar batteries. It seems unlikely that this vehicle, invented by a man named Davidson, actually ran.

It was the invention of the accumulator, around

1880, which made the electric car a feasible proposition. The first in the field appears to have been the Frenchman, Raffard, who converted a Hillman Sociable tricycle to electric propulsion in 1881. Later the same year, Raffard built the first electric four-wheeler of note, which was, in fact, an omnibus.

The Ayrton tricycle appeared in 1882, while in 1887 came the first true electric car. Reported the *Scientific American*: 'In order to please his wife and their little daughter, Mr Magnus Volk, Managing Director of the Brighton Electric Railway in England, had equipped a dog-cart with a ½-horsepower electric motor fed from six storage batteries which ensure six hours of operation'. Volk later entered an electric car in the 1896 Emancipation Day run (or at least a few miles of it).

From then on, the electric cars came thick and fast. In 1888, Immisch of London built an electric carriage for the Sultan of Morocco, constituting the first-ever export of the British motor industry (Volk apparently had a hand in the design of this vehicle), while Ralph Sherrin, of Ramsgate, Kent, who exhibited his first Electric Tricycle at an 1887 cycle exhibition, had gone into production by 1891. Now known as the Vaughan-Sherrin, the company's products also included electric bath chairs.

John Kemp Starley, inventor of the Rover safety bicycle, built a little electric three-wheeler in 1888; motor and accumulators were supplied by Edwell Parker Ltd, of Wolverhampton, whose Bushbury Electric Carts of 1891 (one of which had rein steering!) were fore-runners of the Star Car. Because of the 4 mph speed limit, then prevailing in England, Starley took the car over to Deauville in France, where he

Above: Camille Jenatzy, who held the land-speed record from 1899 to 1902, with his electric car, *Jamais Contente*. The car took the record with a speed of 65.79 mph

Near right: an 1897 Bersey, looking like a horse-drawn carriage except for the steering, which looks somewhat nautical

Far right: a 1901 Columbia electric

Top: a 1902 Baker electric, now owned by the Sköklöster Motor Museum in Sweden

Above: a 1922 Detroit electric brougham which was powered by a 3 hp motor, giving the car a top speed of 25 mph and a range of approximately 125 miles

the world's first driving school on waste ground at Aubervilliers where ex-coachmen were taught to handle these *fiacres électriques* on a 700-metre obstacle course laid with heaps of stones.

The skills acquired on this track were put to good account, no doubt, when the Automobile Club de France organised their motor-cab trials in June 1898. The idea for this event was that of Charles Jeantaud, who, although he had built his first electric vehicle in 1881, did not put it into production until 1893. Among his 1898 models was an electric hansom cab, controlled from a high rear seat. Jeantaud himself drove this machine in the trials, which lasted nine days. The awards in this race were split between the products of Jeantaud and those of his main rival, Kriéger. The sole internal-combustion vehicle in the event, a Peugeot, was so eclipsed that a contemporary pundit, M E. Hospitalier, was moved to declare: 'The petroleum-spirit cab will never be a practicable proposition in large towns'.

However, the electric was becoming the town vehicle for the rich; indeed, as the annual running costs of an electromobile could add up to £300–£700, on maintenance, recharging and wages, it was only the rich who could afford to run them. The more conservative could retain their horse carriage, merely replacing the front wheels with the Heilmann electric *avant-train*, a self-contained driving unit. The Grand Duke Alexis of Russia fitted a Heilmann to his landau in 1898.

It was around this time that the electric car moved into a new sphere of activity, that of record-breaking. As a publicity stunt, Jeantaud built a car which the Comte Chasseloup-Laubat drove over a measured kilometre at Achères at a speed of 39 mph; rival electric car maker Camille Jenatzy beat this with a figure of 41 mph over the same course. With the addition of some modest streamlining, Chasseloup-Laubat raised the record to 58 mph, but soon Jenatzy appeared at Achères with the famous electric racer *La Jamais Contente* (never satisfied).

This was probably the first purpose-built speed car, and featured bullet-shaped coachwork, beaten from Partinium, an early form of aluminium alloy, by the Rheims & Auscher company. The streamlined effect was somewhat marred by the fact that Jenatzy sat on top of the body, with only his legs inside the cockpit; nevertheless, on 29 April 1899, he covered the flying kilometre at a speed of 65.8 mph, the first time that a car had ever exceeded 100 kph. Chasseloup-Laubat, whose car was only an ordinary touring model, did not attempt to better this.

However, the electric sprint car, in which all the power of the batteries was concentrated into one fierce burst of speed, was necessarily a dead-end of development, although Baker in America did achieve remarkable results with his electric racer Torpedo, which resembled a tiny submarine on wheels, with driver and mechanic seated in tandem beneath a glazed 'conning tower', and protected by the first safety belts of automotive history. These proved their worth in a much-publicised crash at a Long Island meeting, in which a spectator was killed when the car swerved into the crowd.

Jenatzy, indeed, abandoned the battery-electric after *La Jamais Contente*, and turned his attention to a new type of vehicle, the petrol-electric, in which a conventional petrol car had its flywheel and transmission replaced by a dynamo supplying current to an electric motor controlled through variable resistances. Among the most successful progenitors of this type of vehicle were two Austrians, Ludwig Lohner and Ferdinand Porsche, who had begun building battery-

managed to career along the sea-front at a breathtaking 8 mph.

However, the great British pioneer of the electric vehicle was Walter Bersey, who built an electric omnibus in 1888, when he was still a teenager. His first cars appeared in 1895, and two of them participated in the London–Brighton Emancipation Day Run the following year, although, as in the case of the Volk Electric, it is unlikely that they ran the entire distance. The major drawback of the electric—the limited range of a vehicle driven by accumulators—was already becoming all too apparent.

As long as the electric car kept within towns, where its accumulators could readily be recharged, it was fine, but it could not be taken touring like a petrol or steam car.

Bersey recognised this fact, and attempted to set up an electric cab service in London in 1897. Despite Royal patronage—the Prince of Wales took a Bersey to Buckingham Palace in 1897—the operation lasted only two years.

In Paris, the Compagnie Générale des Voitures took out a licence to build Bersey cabs and, in 1898, set up

Left: Ford's Comuta, built in 1967 and, *far left*, its chassis, showing the car's four batteries and two traction motors. The Comuta now rests at the Science Museum, London

electrics in 1898 in Vienna. These had their motors incorporated in the front wheel hubs, and it was this principle which Porsche followed on his petrol-electrics (which used Austro-Daimler Mercedes chassis).

'The smooth running of the engine, the musical note of its exhaust, the absence of vibration and, above all, the simplicity of its control', wrote E. W. Hart in 1902, 'are features which must command the favourable judgment of the automobile world. Everything is done electrically, even the starting of the engine. One has only to press the button and the car moves; in fact, so simple is the manipulation of the car that a child could easily be taught to understand it.'

Hart was a Luton business man who had made a fortune out of the manufacture of straw hats, but was to lose it all on electric cars. In 1900, he had built a Lohner-Porsche racing car, *La Toujours Contente*, with a motor in each hub, making it one of the world's first four-wheel-drive cars, predating Spyker by three years; the top speed of this battery-electric racer was 50 mph.

However, Hart, Lohner and Porsche had all lost sight of one important fact: the petrol electric was far more complicated (and thus far more expensive) than a car with conventional transmission and, despite several attempts to revive the petrol-electric over the past twenty years, the only one which enjoyed any success was the Tilling-Stevens passenger vehicle chassis, where the fuel economies achieved by a constant-speed petrol engine on a stop-start service offset the higher first cost of the complex transmission.

Attempts to widen the effective range of battery electrics continued: the euphoniously-named Société de la Voiture Bouquet, Garcin et Schivre, of Neuilly, Seine, built their own batteries and managed to persuade one of their two-seater cars to cover 262 kilometres on one charge in 1900. A year later, the promise of a miracle battery from Thomas Alva Edison raised hopes which were dashed almost at once by the inventor's announcement that the battery would not be ready for some time (and, indeed, it never materialised).

Dominating the British market was the City & Suburban Electric Carriage Company, founded by Paris Singer (son of the sewing machine magnate), whose West End garage could store 800 electromobiles and boast Royal patronage from Queen Alexandra. A

Left: the complicated and heavy workings of an electric car shoe-horned into the back of a Fiat 500. One of the many disadvantages of electric power is that the batteries are so heavy

Left: an Urbania, built in Pisa, Italy. This car weighs 750 pounds, 190 of which are made up by three lead and zinc batteries. It has a top speed of 33 mph and a range of 53 miles. One interesting feature is that the car's body is a turret that can be swivelled round so that the passengers can disembark safely on whatever side of the car they wish

Left: the interior of the electric Fiat 850, which had its electric motor mounted at the rear, in place of the more-normal petrol engine

Right, above and centre: two similar electric-engine layouts on a Fiat 850 and 500 respectively

Below: a Zele 1000 electric car. Due to the very small size of the batteries and motors, the car probably had a very small range and would have been totally impractical

company spokesman dismissed criticisms of the electric's limited range: 'It is possible to travel from London to Glasgow with one of our carriages. Our Surrey phaeton is built for running 120 miles without recharging, whilst our landaulettes can travel from eighty to ninety miles. As you know, there are about 250 electrical charging stations in England alone, so that point cannot be raised as a substantial objection'.

City & Suburban claimed to have overcome most of the snags of operating a battery electric car, with their annual garaging scheme which cost £186. In 1902, they claimed that their business had reached 'gigantic proportions', but, despite this, it had closed down by the end of 1905.

Most European battery-electrics had already vanished by this time, although there were spasmodic attempts to revive the type. What really killed the electric, apart from the insurmountable problem of limited battery range, was the difficulty of repairing the machine when it broke down. 'When the motor proposes to burn up, there is no doubt at all about the fact', wrote Stanley Spooner in 1902. 'It begins to diffuse an agreeable perfume, not very dissimilar to the smell of incense.' This, apparently, was the shellac insulation of the windings going up in smoke, the only solution being to have the motor rewound. Added Spooner: 'An armature winder is a skilled mechanic, who commands high wages and puts on airs'.

In America, where a poor road system kept most motorists within city limits, the electric lasted far longer than in Europe. Indeed, Detroit Electrics were still available to special order as late as 1939, their wooden artillery wheels contrasting oddly with the Dodge coachwork they used for cheapness of production, despite their inherent weakness.

That, apart from a few vehicles built to overcome 1940s petrol rationing, was the end of the electric car, although it survived, in 1974, for short-haul urban delivery vehicles, such as milk-floats.

In the 1960s and '70s, there was a revival in interest, due to petrol shortages and increased city-centre congestion, and several prototypes were built. In the late 1960s, Ford built a tiny city-car called the Comuta, and more recently Enfield have produced a similar type of vehicle, but still the old bogey of battery capacity looms large. Indeed, these vehicles have no greater range than their counterparts of seventy years ago.

The 'no-pollution' characteristics of the electric may be a myth, too. Ford has pointed out that the power station which provides the charge for the car's batteries may be a considerable source of localised pollution, covering a neighbourhood with the fall-out from burning oil or coke. However, the nuclear reactor can dispense with this type of pollution, as can hydraulically-powered generators. New batteries are always under design or trial and the answer may well lie in making use of the sun's enormous energy to generate electricity. DBW

'Elle va-she goes!'

During its short life, the Elva company produced some interesting and successful cars, and is one of only a few British companies who have made an impact on the American motor-racing scene, which has usually been dominated by home-bred machinery

SOON AFTER WORLD WAR II, Frank Nichols opened a garage in Bexhill-on-Sea, Sussex, where he specialised in sporting machinery. He had a short competition career himself but then decided to go into car manufacture. His first car—called the CSM Special, after his garage, Chapman Sports Motors—was a Ford Ten-engined two-seater. It showed some promise,

Top: the pretty Elva 160XS, of which only three were built in 1964. Two were powered by BMW 1800 engines, one being used as a road car and the other for competition, while the third had a 3.5-litre Buick unit

Above: the beautiful Mk 8-BMW 2-litre. The car was very successful in British Club racing, particularly in the hands of Tony Lanfranchi

so Nichols decided to form a separate company to build sports-racing cars. This was called Elva Engineering, the name Elva being a contraction of the French 'elle va'—she goes.

The first Elva was produced in 1955, this car being a smart two-seater with all-enveloping aluminium body-work. The chassis was of the multi-tubular type pioneered in Britain by Lotus, but the other mechanical components were an amalgam of standard and modified production-car parts, as the British racing-car industry had not yet got into full swing. The engine was the ubiquitous Ford Ten unit cleverly modified to use overhead-inlet valves instead of side valves. This conversion was designed in conjunction with the noted engine tuner, Harry Weslake, who worked nearby at Rye, and it was to become a very popular conversion both for racing and road cars.

Two examples of this car were built and raced with

some success, and soon orders began to trickle in from racing drivers. A Mk 1B model, which incorporated a number of improvements, was built during 1956, and in 1957 the Mk 2 was announced.

Although different engines could be fitted, the Mk 1B and 2 were usually supplied with the popular 1098 cc Coventry Climax engine, mated to a four-speed MG gearbox. The Mk2 became one of the fastest small-capacity sports cars in Britain, especially in the hands of Archie Scott-Brown who won a number of races with the car, and established class lap records.

Sales of the Mk 1B and Mk 2 soared, especially in the USA where a number of drivers bought them and won a great many races in the Sports Car Club of America racing series.

A process of steady development was now undertaken and the Mk3 featured a neat proprietary glass-fibre all-enveloping body which was cheaper and easier to make than the hand-made bodies. This model retained the Coventry Climax engine, although Archie Scott-Brown raced a works car fitted with the complicated Butterworth flap-valve engine, which proved to be powerful but unreliable.

The Mk 4 of 1958 was a radical departure from the Mk2 and 3 designs as the de Dion near suspension was abandoned in favour of a pure independent system using transverse box section radius arms, with the tubular drive shaft acting as the upper locating member. The drum brakes were mounted inboard, adjacent to the differential, as on the Mk 2, and the remainder of the specification was rather similar to the Mk2 and 3 except that a good deal of weight had been saved. It featured an aluminium body and was again powered by the Coventry Climax engine, mated to the MG gearbox, but some owners fitted MG or Ford engines.

By 1958, Nichols was receiving constant enquiries about the possibility of building a road-going sports car, mainly from America where the importers were very keen. So he designed and produced the Courier in a very short space of time. This car featured a twin-tube chassis frame with $2\frac{1}{2}$ in diameter main logitudinal tubes, and cross bracing members of $1\frac{1}{4}$ in tubing; additional small tubing superstructures were fitted for the front suspension, scuttle and rear suspension. The front suspension was by Elva-manufactured double wishbones and coil springs, while a Wolseley 1500 rear axle was fitted, suspension being by coil spring/damper units with location by twin trailing arms and a Panhard rod. Lockheed drum brakes were fitted on all four wheels, rack and pinion steering from the Morris Minor was used and the power unit was the BMC 'B' series engine used in the MGA; originally a 1489 cc version was used but this was later increased to 1588 cc, in which form this four-cylinder unit gave around 70 bhp. It was mated to the standard four speed MG gearbox. The prototype was built with an aluminium body but it was decided to use glassfibre for production models and Elva set up a glassfibre shop at the factory.

597

This attractive-looking car was an immediate hit in the USA and sales were restricted to export markets for some time, but it eventually became available in Britain where it was marketed as a kit car, and again attracted a favourable reaction. Naturally, many drivers turned the Courier into a racing machine and it became a very popular car in American production-car racing where it set many drivers on their racing careers. Mark Donohue, who later won the Indianapolis 500 and many other races, won the US Road Racing Championship in an Elva Courier at the start of his career.

On the racing side, the Mk 5 succeeded the Mk 4 in 1959, the design being fairly similar apart from bodywork changes, but a more important step was a single-seater derivative of the Mk 5 for the then new Formula Junior. This car was one of the first cars ready for the new Formula; like all other Elvas, it was front-engined, although the trend was towards rear engines, but the space frame chassis was neatly made and, with its attractive mini-Vanwall body, it gained a lot of attention when it first raced at Snetterton in April. The car gained a few good wins and orders began to pour in, especially from America. The two-stroke DKW engine was showing-up well on the Continent and Nichols procured a number of these for his FJ cars, but it was a troublesome unit as it was difficult to cool properly. Although Chris Threlfall gave the car some good wins, it tended to lose ground to more modern rear-engined makes, especially after Threlfall was killed in a race at Aix-Les-Bains. Despite the car's ultimate eclipse, Elva sold over 150, largely because it was readily available as a kit of parts.

The company went through financial problems in 1961 and, out of the crisis, a new company called Elva Cars (1961) Ltd was formed. A new rear-engined Formula Junior car was designed for the 1961 season and, for the first time, a rear-engined sports/racing car, the Mk 6, was announced. Both cars were available with the Cosworth-modified Ford Anglia engines, the sports car gaining a number of wins and selling in fair quantities; but the FJ car was a relative failure and, by 1962, Elva had virtually abandoned building single-seater racing cars.

The Courier was selling well but its production took up a great deal of time so, in 1962, Nichols made an agreement with Trojan Ltd of Purley, Surrey for them to build the car under licence.

Nichols was now free to concentrate on racing cars and, for 1963, he produced the Mk 7 sports/racing car which retained many features from the Mk 6. A variety of engines could be ordered; the FWA Coventry Climax engine was still popular but the Mk 7 was also available with the Cosworth-Ford 1100 cc unit or the Twin-Cam Cosworth-Ford 1½-litre unit. Using this latter engine, Bill Moss won a number of races in the works car.

For 1964, the Mk 8 Elva was produced; it remained much the same as the Mk 7 but it was available with a wide range of engines from a 997 cc Ford Anglia up to the 2-litre BMW and Porsche engines and, with a Porsche unit, Herbert Muller finished a close second in the European Mountain Championship to the factory Porsche of Edgar Barth. In Britain, the BMW unit was most popular and this 2-litre unit, when tuned by Frank Webb, gave around 190 bhp. This was sufficient to give Tony Lanfranchi many wins in British club races. A large number of Mk 8s were sold and private owners gained many successes around the world. A road version of the Mk 8, known as the 160XS, with bodywork designed by Fiore, was marketed, but only three cars were produced.

By 1964, the Trojan Group had taken over the whole of the Elva concern, and production of the racing cars was eventually moved to the Purley factory, although Nichols remained as a consultant. A deal was made with Bruce McLaren for Trojan to build the New Zealander's new Oldsmobile-powered sports car under the name McLaren-Elva in order to cash in on the good name that Elva had built up in the USA.

Demand for the Courier was beginning to run down despite the fact that Trojan developed a handsome new sports body in 1964, together with an improved chassis and the option of the 1½-litre Ford engine as an alternative to the MGB 1.8-litre unit. This model had independent rear suspension double wishbones and a new occasional four-seater coupé was also announced. A sports/racing version called the Sebring was announced, this version having a lightweight body, magnesium wheels, a limited slip differential, and the option of highly-tuned Cosworth-Ford or MGB engines. But it, too, had little success and in 1966 Trojan sold the Courier project to Ken Sheppard Customised Sports Cars of Radlett. This firm continued production spasmodically until 1969, when the remaining spare parts were sold to Tony Ellis of Windsor. One last ditch effort was made with the introduction of a 3-litre, high performance coupé called the Cougar. It was powered by a Ford V6 engine with a Minnow fish-type carburettor which enabled the car to reach 130 mph and accelerate to 100 mph in just over 20 seconds. The Cougar was styled very much in the 1950s tradition, resembling early Bristol models. Perhaps this was the deciding factor that killed Elva: the car never caught on, and Tony Ellis concentrated on a spares and repair service until 1973.

So, the Elva name finally died for good in 1966 and Frank Nichols returned to his garage and general engineering business after a colourful, if short, life as a racing car manufacturer. MT

Top: the Elva Formula Junior car of 1962 was powered by a Cosworth-tuned Ford Anglia engine. The car, however, was never a success and the company stopped manufacturing single seaters the following year

Above: Elva's most successful model was probably the Courier sports car. The car, powered by a BMC B-series engine, was a big hit in the USA, where many owners used their cars for racing

FROM ARMAMENTS TO ASTON MARTINS

Enfield were well known as armament and cycle manufacturers before they entered the motoring field, but they produced some interesting and well made cars

Right: the Enfield 'Nimble Nine' model of 1913 was fitted with a four-cylinder engine, developing 9 hp

Below: the 1923 Enfield-Allday 200-Mile Race car with driver J. Chance at the wheel

'MADE LIKE A GUN' was the proud slogan of the Enfield Cycle Company of Redditch, Worcestershire, who were well known as armament and cycle manufacturers long before they became involved with motor vehicles. Their first powered vehicle, of 1900, was decidedly unambitious—a light motor cycle with the engine mounted in front of the steering head, driving the rear wheel through a crossed belt—but the company had soon progressed to two-wheelers of a more substantial nature, with the engine in the more conventional position. From motor cycles, it was only a short step to motor quadricycles, one of which was Henry Royce's first vehicle.

These early Royal Enfields generally used De Dion engines of $2\frac{3}{4}$ and $3\frac{1}{2}$ hp, though the company did produce their own power units, one of which was water-cooled, with the final drive by chain from the timing shaft.

By 1904, Royal Enfield were building motor cars: initially a range of two models was marketed, both built on orthodox lines. The 6 hp two-seater had a De Dion single-cylinder engine and was, claimed the makers, specially constructed for heavy work and hilly districts; its specification included a three-speed gearbox and 'three brakes'. Prices started from £175.

The 10 hp, which cost £300 (£325 with leather upholstery and 'Modèle Riche' finish), was a twin-cylinder four-seater with a honeycomb radiator augmented by a water tank on the dashboard. Both cars had tubular chassis, that of the larger car being braced to stop the machine from folding in the middle.

In 1906, the car-manufacturing operation became independent of the parent company, and began production of a more substantial range of cars, designed by E. H. Lancaster. These were a 4.1-litre 16/20 hp and a 5.9-litre 24/30 hp. Both had four-cylinder engines, pressed-steel chassis and live-axle final drive, there were three powerful metal-to-metal compression brakes, and the Enfield radiator incorporated 1200 round tubes for maximum cooling.

Accessibility was a feature of the design—the clutch could, it was claimed, be dismantled without disturbing the engine or gearbox, while the gearshafts ran on ball bearings, and could be reached through large inspection plates at the top and bottom of the gearbox. Ignition was by coil and battery, rather than the more up-to-date magneto, and the 16/20 cost £420 complete, while the 24/30 was £480 as a chassis, £525 including coachwork.

The following year, a smaller 15 hp model replaced the 16/20; it was, however, short-lived, for at the Olympia Show in November 1907, the stand was occupied by four 18/22 hp Enfields, at prices ranging from £341 for the bare chassis to £407 for the Standard Car with detachable top, back and centre lights—an ideal car for town and country.

But these cars were not what they seemed, for a glance at the power units revealed that these were

identical to those fitted to the 20/25 Alldays & Onions
—the independent existence of the Enfield Autocar
Company had lasted less than two years before failing
finances had led to their takeover by the Alldays &
Onions Pneumatic Engineering Company of Birmingham, an engineering firm which could trace its origins
back as far as the mid 1600s and had produced its first
car, a wheel-steered quadricycle, in 1898.

Thereafter, the Enfield range was composed of de-
luxe versions of Alldays models; in mid 1908, the
company moved from its works at Hunt End, Redditch, to a factory at Fallows Road, Sparkbrook,
Birmingham.

The first three models from the new factory were
shown at Olympia in November 1908. They consisted
of the 10/12 hp Popular two-cylinder, price 212
guineas (this little voiturette had originally been introduced by Alldays in 1905, and survived until 1913), the
18/24 and a survival from the past in the shape of an
updated 30/35, the only one of the Lancaster designs to
survive the takeover, and one which had no Alldays
counterpart. The fourth model in the range, the 16 hp
four, was not at the Show.

Two new models appeared in the 1911 line-up: a
12 hp light four based on the new Alldays and a 20 hp.
Later that year, the company attempted to break into
the cyclecar market with the Autorette, a two-cylinder,
two-speed three-wheeler retailing at £95, but it was
soon replaced by the more conventional—and costly—
7/8 hp, vee-twin Autolette four-wheeler with worm
final drive. From 1911 on, the four-cylinder models
were available with a self starter. Dynamo lighting
appeared in 1913.

Sales of the Autolette during 1913 were encouraging
enough for the company to launch a 9 hp four-cylinder
variant at the end of the year, priced at £158 against the
twin's £138; this model became the famous Nimble
Nine in 1914, by which time the company was
switching over to White & Poppe proprietary engines
for the larger 14.3 hp and 18.4 hp cars. Unusually for
the period, Enfield built their own bodies, adopting a
pleasingly ungainly flush-sided torpedo line for 1914;
special coachwork was normally supplied by Mulliners.

Rationalisation was carried to its logical conclusion
after the war, with Alldays and Enfield merging as
Enfield-Allday Motors Limited, based at Sparkbrook.
But in place of the modestly-priced, ultra-conservative
family cars of the pre-war era, the company proposed
a complete breakaway from established canons of car
design. Their 1919 Bullet was largely the work of A. W.
Reeves, who had designed the famous 25 hp RFC
model Crossley; he was aided by A. C. Bertelli,
Enfield-Allday's works manager. The Bullet drew
heavily on wartime aero-engine developments, and
featured a five-cylinder radial engine mounted in a
triangulated chassis carried on long cantilever springs.
The gearbox was mounted at the apices of the chassis
side-members, and the air-cooled engine could be
rotated for servicing requirements by just undoing a
couple of bolts. The power unit featured curious
concentric inlet and exhaust valves, claimed to give the
maximum in efficiency, though 23 bhp from a 2.5-litre
engine was hardly inspiring, even in 1919, as by now
the development of the motor car was well under way.
All-up weight was said to be as low as 9.75 cwt,
contributing to a 40 mpg petrol consumption, but the
new car was too complex for economy of production.
The price was originally £350, but this kept going up,
for the design was unsuitable for mass production.
Total output was perhaps four cars, and a larger 15 hp
version with a six-cylinder sleeve-valve engine and
more orthodox chassis and suspension does not seem

to have passed the artist's impression stage.

Bertelli hurriedly designed a replacement, a conventional four-cylinder car with inclined side valves,
remarkable only for its quality of finish—'Never before
has such skill, material and fine workmanship been put
into a light car', boasted the company. But once again,
the design was not suited to economical production,
and only a hundred or so of the 10/20 and 12/30
Enfield-Alldays were built before production ended
in 1925 and the company's final factory, at Small
Heath, Birmingham, closed down.

The model had enjoyed some modest sporting
successes, so Bertelli attempted to strike out on his
own with a sports car—the Remington & Bertelli—
which had an overhead camshaft 1.5-litre engine in a
racing Enfield-Allday chassis; but in 1926 he acquired
the moribund Aston Martin company from Lionel
Martin, and this Remington & Bertelli formed the
basis of the Aston Martins built between 1926 and
1929 in Feltham, Middlesex.   DBW

Top: at the end of 1913,
Enfield launched a four-
cylinder, 9 hp model
priced at £158. This
became known as the
'Nimble Nine'. The car
was a two-seater tourer
and the bodies were
produced by Enfield
itself

Above: the 1922 200-
Mile Race Enfield-Allday

This magnificent four-color encyclopedia is brought to you by Columbia House
in cooperation with Orbis Publishing Ltd., one of Great Britain's most enterprising publishers.
Rather than change any of the encyclopedia's authoritative international automotive text, we have
included a glossary of terms that will give you immediate American equivalents, a conversion table
for the international metric system, and a conversion table for equivalent monetary values.

Glossary

BRITISH	AMERICAN	BRITISH	AMERICAN
Aerial	Antenna	Motor	Engine
Aluminium	Aluminum	Number plate	License plate
Apron	Skirt	Overrider	Bumper guard
Big-end	Rod (conrod) bearing	Paraffin	Kerosene
Blower *(colloquial)*	Supercharger	Parking brake	Parking lock
Bonnet	Hood	Petrol	Gasoline, "gas"
Boot	Trunk	Petrol pump	Gasoline or fuel pump
Brake servo	Power brake	Production car	Stock car
Bulkhead	Firewall	Propellor shaft	Drive shaft
Capacity	Displacement	Quarter light	Door vent
Carburetter; carburettor	Carburetor		
Check strap	Door stop	Rear lamp	Tail light
Clutch release bearing	Clutch throwout bearing	Rear seat squab	Rear setback or backrest
Control box	Voltage regulator	Reverse lamp	Back up light
Crown wheel and pinion	Ring gear and pinion	Roof lamp	Dome light
Cylinder block	Cylinder crankcase	Saloon	Sedan
Dip switch	Dimmer switch	Scuttle	Cowl
Door pillar	Door post	Selector rod	Shift bar
Drop arm	Pitman arm	Servo-assisted	Power assisted
Drop-head	Convertible	Side lamp	Parking light
Dynamo	Generator	Side member	Side rail
Epicylic gearbox	Planetary gearbox	Spanner	Wrench
Exhaust silencer	Muffler	Sparking plug	Spark plug
Facia panel	Dashboard	Starting handle	Crank handle
		Steering column	Steering post
Gear lever	Gear shift lever	Steering relay	Steering idler
Gearbox	Transmission	Stub axle	Steering knuckle
Gearbox housing	Transmission casing	Sump	Pan
Gearchange	Gearshift	Swivel pin	King pin
Glassfibre	Fiberglass	Toe board	Toe pan
Grease nipple	Grease fitting	Track	Tread
Gudgeon pin	Piston or wrist pin	Track rod	Tie bar or track bar
Half shaft	Axle shaft	Two-stroke	Two-cycle
Handbrake	Parking brake	Tyre	Tire
Hose clip	Hose clamp	Valance	Rocker panel
Ignition harness	Ignition set	Wheel arch	Wheelhouse or housing
Kerb	Curb	Wheel brace	Wheel wrench
		Windscreen	Windshield
Layshaft	Counter shaft	Wing	Fender
Main shaft	Output shaft	Wishbone	A-arm; Control arm
Marque	Brand, make	Works	Plant, factory

Metric Equivalents
(Based on National Bureau of Standards)

Length

Centimeter (Cm.)	= 0.3937 in.	In.	= 2.5400 cm.
Meter (M.)	= 3.2808 ft.	Ft.	= 0.3048 m.
Meter	= 1.0936 yd.	Yd.	= 0.9144 m.
Kilometer (Km.)	= 0.6214 mile	Mile	= 1.6093 km.

Area

Sq. cm.	= 0.1550 sq. in.	Sq. in.	= 6.4516 sq. cm.
Sq. m.	= 10.7639 sq. ft.	Sq. ft.	= 0.0929 sq. m.
Sq. m.	= 1.1960 sq. yd.	Sq. yd.	= 0.8361 sq. m.
Hectare	= 2.4710 acres	Acre	= 0.4047 hectar
Sq. km.	= 0.3861 sq. mile	Sq. mile	= 2.5900 sq. km.

Volume

Cu. cm.	= 0.0610 cu. in.	Cu. in.	= 16.3872 cu. cm.
Cu. m.	= 35.3145 cu. ft.	Cu. ft.	= 0.0283 cu. m.
Cu. m.	= 1.3079 cu. yd.	Cu. yd.	= 0.7646 cu. m.

Capacity

Liter	= 61.0250 cu. in.	Cu. in.	= 0.0164 liter
Liter	= 0.0353 cu. ft.	Cu. ft.	= 28.3162 liters
Liter	= 0.2642 gal. (U.S.)	Gal.	= 3.7853 liters
Liter	= 0.0284 bu. (U.S.)	Bu.	= 35.2383 liters

Liter = {
1000.027 cu. cm.
1.0567 qt. (liquid) or 0.9081 qt. (dry)
2.2046 lb. of pure water at 4 C = 1 kg.
}

Weight

Gram. (Gm.)	= 15.4324 grains	Grain	= 0.0648 gm.
Gram	= 0.0353 oz.	Oz.	= 28.3495 gm.
Kilogram (Kg.)	= 2.2046 lb.	Lb.	= 0.4536 kg.
Kg.	= 0.0011 ton (sht.)	Ton (sht.)	= 907.1848 kg.
Ton (met.)	= 1.1023 ton (sht.)	Ton (sht.)	= 0.9072 ton (met.)
Ton (met.)	= 0.9842 ton (lg.)	Ton (lg.)	= 1.0160 ton (met.)

Pressure

1 kg. per sq. cm.	= 14.223 lb. per sq. in.
1 lb. per sq. in.	= 0.0703 kg. per sq. cm.
1 kg. per sq. m.	= 0.2048 lb. per sq. ft.
1 lb. per sq. ft.	= 4.8824 kg. per sq. m.
1 kg. per sq. cm.	= 0.9678 normal atmosphere

1 normal atmosphere = {
1.0332 kg. per sq. cm.
1.0133 bars
14.696 lb. per sq. in.
}

Approximate Values of the Pound (£)
in terms of U.S. Dollars ($)

1914-1919	$4.76
1935	4.90
1936	4.97
1937	4.94
1938	4.89
1939	4.46
1940-1949	4.03
1950-1967	2.80
1968-1970	2.40
1971-1972	$2.40/2.60
1972-Present	2.60/2.10